DATE DUE

Growing Up with
SCIENCE®

Third Edition

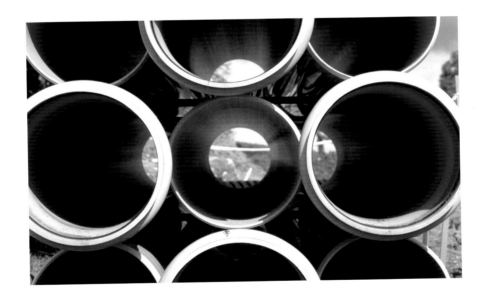

10

Optics–Plant kingdom

Marshall Cavendish
Reference
New York

Marshall Cavendish
99 White Plains Road
Tarrytown, NY 10591

www.marshallcavendish.us

© 2006 Marshall Cavendish Corporation
© 1987, 1990 Marshall Cavendish Limited

GROWING UP WITH SCIENCE is a registered trademark
of Marshall Cavendish Corporation

Library of Congress Cataloging-in-Publication Data

Growing up with science.— 3rd ed.
    p. cm.
    Includes index.
    Contents: v. 1. Abrasive-Astronomy — v. 2. Atmosphere-Cable television —
v. 3. Cable travel-Cotton — v. 4. Crane-Electricity — v. 5 Electric motor-
Friction — v. 6. Fuel cell-Immune system — v. 7. Induction-Magnetism —
v. 8. Mapmaking-Mining and quarrying — v. 9. Missile and torpedo-Oil
exploration and refining — v. 10. Optics-Plant kingdom — v. 11. Plasma
physics-Radiotherapy — v. 12. Railroad system-Seismology — v. 13.
Semiconductor-Sports — v. 14. Spring-Thermography — v. 15. Thermometer-
Virus, biological — v. 16. Virus, computer-Zoology — v. 17. Index.
    ISBN 0-7614-7505-2 (set)
    ISBN 0-7614-7515-X (vol. 10)
    1. Science—Encyclopedias.

Q121.G764 2006
503—dc22

                                              2004049962
                        09 08 07 06 05 6 5 4 3 2 1

Printed in China

CONSULTANT

Donald R. Franceschetti, Ph.D.
Dunavant Professor at the University of Memphis

Donald R. Franceschetti is a member of the American
Chemical Society, the American Physical Society, the
Cognitive Science Society, the History of Science Society,
and the Society for Neuroscience.

CONTRIBUTORS TO VOLUME 10

Sarah Evans   Jim Martin
John Farndon   Ben Hume-Paton
Tom Jackson

Marshall Cavendish

Editors: Peter Mavrikis and Susan Rescigno
Editorial Director: Paul Bernabeo
Production Manager: Alan Tsai

The Brown Reference Group

Editors: Leon Gray and Simon Hall
Designer: Sarah Williams
Picture Researcher: Helen Simm
Indexer: Kay Ollerenshaw
Illustrators: Darren Awuah and Mark Walker
Managing Editor: Bridget Giles
Art Director: Dave Goodman

CONTENTS

KEY TO COLOR CODING OF ARTICLES

■ EARTH, SPACE, AND ENVIRONMENTAL SCIENCES

■ LIFE SCIENCES AND MEDICINE

■ MATHEMATICS

□ PHYSICS AND CHEMISTRY

■ TECHNOLOGY

■ PEOPLE

Optics

Optics is the study of how light behaves, and what happens to light when it reflects off surfaces, or passes through them. Optics is partly concerned with vision—the way people's eyes see things—and partly with lenses and mirrors that direct light in a particular way.

If you look at the beam from a flashlight or a spotlight in the dark, you will see that light rays travel in straight lines. This principle is the most basic rule in optics. It allows scientists to plot the path of light rays on paper simply by drawing lines against a ruler. The light ray will change course only when it hits something. Even then, it will continue on its new path in a straight line.

Shadows

When light rays hit an object, they bounce off, are absorbed, or pass through. Substances like glass, which let light pass through them, are said to be transparent. Substances that scatter light on the way through, like frosted glass, are said to be translucent. Those that stop light altogether are said to be opaque. Light always travels in straight lines, so when it hits an opaque object, it cannot flow around it like water around a rock in a stream; it can only travel straight past, casting a shadow behind the object where the light path is blocked.

If a person holds his or her hand up to the Sun, or to a bright desk lamp, he or she will see that the light casts two kinds of shadows. In the middle is a dark shadow called the umbra, where light rays are blocked off completely. Around the edge is a lighter penumbra, where some light reaches, as light rays are bent slightly around the edge of the hand.

Reflection and mirrors

When light strikes a surface, some or all of it is reflected. From most surfaces, it is scattered in all directions. With mirrors and other smooth shiny surfaces, every ray may bounce off in exactly the same pattern as it arrives. The result is a perfect reflection of the light source, or a mirror image.

Light bounces off a mirror in the same way a ball bounces off a wall—bouncing off at exactly the same angle as it strikes. The light ray that strikes a surface is called the incident ray, and the angle which it makes with a line perpendicular to the

◄ The rainbow in this photograph has formed because of the optical properties of raindrops. When sunlight hits raindrops at the correct angle, the drops act as prisms, splitting the sunlight into the colors of the spectrum.

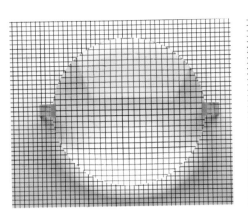 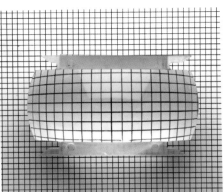 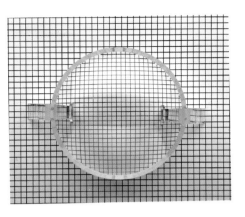

▲ *The squares on the graph paper show the effect of different lens shapes on light rays. Convex lenses can produce slight to strong magnification (left and center). Concave lenses produce a slight reduction (right).*

▶ *This diagram shows how a microscope uses lenses to magnify a tiny object. Light from the object comes through the objective lens, which forms a magnified image inside the microscope. The eyepiece lens then magnifies that image again to make a final image that is much larger than the original object.*

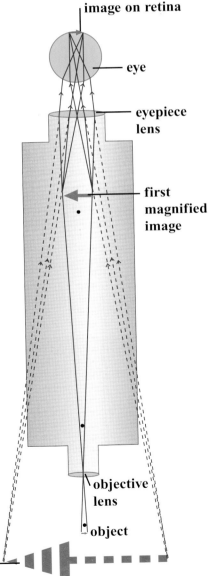

image on retina

eye

eyepiece lens

first magnified image

objective lens

object

second magnified image

DID YOU KNOW?

On a hot day, what looks like a small lake may appear ahead on the freeway. This is, in fact, an image of the sky, called a mirage. Light from the sky is refracted by the hot air and thus seems to come from the road.

surface is called the angle of incidence. The angle that the reflected ray makes with the same line is called the angle of reflection. There is a basic law of reflection, which states that the angle of incidence equals the angle of reflection.

When a person looks in a mirror, it as if there is another identical world behind the mirror. This image is called a virtual image. In a good, flat or "plane" mirror, the virtual image is effectively identical to the real thing. The only real difference is that the image is completely reversed from side to side, so that a person's right hand becomes his or her left hand in the mirror image, and vice versa. This effect is called lateral inversion, or mirror image.

With curved mirrors, the image is not only reversed, but it also looks bigger or smaller. A convex (bowed out) mirror produces a smaller image. A concave (dished) mirror produces a larger image of a nearby object and a smaller, upside-down image of a distant object.

Refraction and lenses

When light passes through something transparent, like glass or water, the rays bend as the light slows down. This bending is called refraction, and it explains why swimming pools sometimes look shallower than they really are, and why spoons appear bent when standing in a glass of water.

Both refraction and reflection occur because light travels at different speeds through different transparent materials. It travels at more than 186,000 miles (300,000 kilometers) per second in air. But when it moves into glass or water, it slows down. Light, therefore, changes direction if it strikes at an angle. It is a little like a car spinning around when one wheel runs onto a patch of sand.

Just as there is a law of reflection, so there are laws of refraction. The key law is that for each kind of glass, the ratio between the sine of the angle of incidence—the angle at which a light ray strikes the glass—and the sine of the angle at which it is refracted, is always the same. In other words, the glass always refracts light by the same amount. This law was first discovered by the Dutch physicist Willebrord Snell (1580–1626) in 1621, and it is called Snell's law. This unchanging ratio is known as the glass's "refractive index."

When a light ray passes from air to water, refraction always occurs, no matter what the angle of incidence is. When a ray passes from water to air, refraction sometimes does not occur. As the angle of incidence increases, the refracted ray comes out closer to the water's surface. At a certain "critical angle" of incidence, the refracted ray travels along the surface at an angle of refraction of 90 degrees. When the angle of incidence is increased further,

no light is refracted at all. It is all reflected back into the water. This is called total internal reflection and is used in several optical instruments, in particular binoculars. Binoculars contain prisms that use total internal reflection to "fold" the light path and increase the focal length. A whole new branch of optics, called fiber optics, depends on the internal reflection of light rays within fine glass fibers.

Lenses

Flat glass always refracts light at the same angle, but if glass is given a curved surface, it can be made to refract at different angles. In this way, light rays can be made to bend closer and closer together (converge) or farther and farther apart (diverge). Lenses are carefully curved pieces of glass that use this effect to create a particular image.

There are two kinds of lens: concave and convex. A convex lens is thick in the middle and thin at the edge. It makes light rays converge, concentrating them at a point called the focus. By bringing light rays together, it makes the image larger, magnifying it. A concave lens, on the other hand, is thin in the middle and thick at the edge. It makes light rays diverge or spread out, so they look smaller.

Every optical instrument, from a magnifying glass to an astronomical telescope, uses combinations of lenses and mirrors to reflect and refract light to create the desired image. In the past, lens makers perfected the shape of their lenses largely by trial and error, grinding glass little by little until it was

▶ *This fantastic display of laser and conventional lights shows just how geometric a pattern light rays create. The straight red rays are laser beams. The blue beams are spread by the process of diffraction.*

right. Now, computers can be used to plot the path of light rays from every possible shape and combination of lens, and instruct machines to grind the glass into exactly the right shape.

Simple lenses suffer from faults known as aberrations. The two main kinds of aberrations are spherical and chromatic. Spherical aberration results from making a lens simply from part of a sphere of glass, rather than shaping the curve bit by bit, which is very costly. The result is that the edges and the center of the lens focus light at slightly different points, making the image blurred. Chromatic aberration occurs because different colors of light travel at slightly different speeds, so they are each refracted by a lens to a different degree. The result is that they focus at slightly different distances from the lens. Again, the result is a slight blurring of the image. A lens designer's job is to minimize aberrations—usually by combining lenses so that one corrects the faults of the other.

Branches of optics

The optics of lenses and visions is concerned only with light rays traveling in straight lines that can be plotted using geometry to calculate angles of reflection and refraction. This is called geometrical optics. But light does not just travel in rays; it moves in waves, too, not like waves in the sea, but vibrations of energy. The study of light waves is called physical optics. Because light waves also travel as tiny particles of energy called photons, a third branch of optics, quantum optics, studies particles of light.

Physical optics

We know light travels in waves because certain things happen to it that could only happen if light is a wave. Sometimes, two beams of light join to produce not light but darkness. This effect is called interference and occurs when two identical light waves meet exactly half a wave out of step. They cancel each other out because the crest of one wave coincides with the trough of the other.

Another wave effect is diffraction. This is the breaking up and spreading out of light waves when they pass through a very narrow slit. The result is that light spills around the edge of the slit and does not cast a sharp shadow.

A third wave effect is polarization. Light waves typically vibrate at right angles to the direction in which they are traveling—but in all planes (to the left and right, up and down). Certain crystals and synthetic plastics act like filters and can cut out all vibrations except those in one plane. If light is passed through two polarizing filters, one after the other, and the filters are rotated, in one position they will totally block off the light.

Quantum optics

Even waves cannot explain things about light such as the interaction of light with matter. When light falls on a metal such as selenium, electrons are given out. This fact is used in photoelectric cells, and it is called the photoelectric effect. It is explained by treating light as a stream of photons. The photons knock the electrons away from their atoms. The explanation of other ways that light can act, such as fluorescence and phosphorescence and the production of laser light, also relies on the idea of photons. It plays a major part in quantum theory, developed by the German physicist Max Planck (1858–1947) a century ago.

See also: LIGHT • REFLECTION AND REFRACTION

Optoelectronics

Optoelectronics is a developing branch of science and technology that focuses on how electronics can be used to manipulate light. The most familiar examples of optoelectronics are digital cameras and displays for computers and TVs, but they are also important in industry, medicine, and space travel.

Optoelectronics is one of the fastest developing areas of technology, as scientists are constantly discovering new ways in which light can be manipulated electronically. Optoelectronics often comes under the heading of photonics—the study of all technology that uses light. Photons are the tiny "bundles" of energy that make up a light beam.

Optoelectronics is really divided into three, often overlapping, areas: devices that give out light, such as light emitting diodes (LEDs), liquid crystal displays (LCDs), and especially lasers; devices that detect light, including digital cameras, scanners, and medical imaging technology; and devices that transmit light for telecommunications.

Photonic telecommunications

The most dramatic developments in photonics and optoelectronics are in the telecommunications industry, and in particular fiber optics. Fiber optic cables are cables made from bundles of glasslike fibers that transmit laser beams by reflecting them off their internal surfaces. Words and pictures, speech, music, video, the Internet, and many other kinds of data are turned into pulses of laser light and then bounced down the fiber optic cable at the speed of light.

Fiber-optic cables can carry a huge amount of data, much more than the conventional copper cables used to carry electrical signals, and at much higher speeds. Optic cables can transmit data across the world in a fraction of a second.

Already, millions of miles of fiber optic cables are being laid around the world and under the sea. The first undersea optic cable could carry more data than all the copper cables in the world ever have. As the Internet begins to use optoelectronic technology, it is getting faster and faster. Today, most of the big, long distance connections are fiber optics. But soon fiber optics will link right into most homes, enabling things such as interactive TV on your computer. When this happens, there will be no need for satellite dishes and TV aerials; everything will come into the home through an Internet connection.

◀ *Flat-screen liquid crystal displays (LCDs), such as this one used by a laptop computer, are a recent innovation in optoelectronics. In the future, however, computers themselves may operate using light. These machines will be smaller, faster, and more powerful than ever before.*

◄ *Rescue workers, such as this firefighter, rely on thermal imaging devices, which use optoelectronics. These devices detect the infrared light given off by warm objects, such as bodies, allowing rescue workers to find people in pitch darkness or smoke.*

Photonic crystals and light-emitting transistors

In the late 1980s, U.S. physicist Eli Yablonovitch and others discovered how to fabricate special structures, called photonic crystals, that can do to light what semiconductors do to electricity. Semiconductors are materials like silicon that transmit electricity only under certain conditions, and they form the basis of transistors, silicon chips, and all electronic devices. Photonic crystals do exactly the same, transmitting light only under certain conditions.

Scientists hope to replace semiconductors and electricity with photonic crystals and beams of light to create computers and other electronic devices that run on light. Since light travels much faster than electricity (the speed of light is 186,000 miles or 300,000 kilometers per second), computers running on light would be extremely fast. Since photons of light are also very tiny and have effectively no mass, these computers could also be incredibly small and light.

What could be another key discovery in optoelectronics was made in 2004 by U.S. electrical engineer Nick Holonyak (1928–), the inventor of the LED, and Taiwanese-born U.S. electrical engineer Milton Feng (1950–) at Illinois University. Holonyak and Feng found a cross between an LED and a transistor—a light-emitting transistor. This could provide a simple link between light signals and electronic signals.

Optoelectronic imaging and sensing advances

New optoelectronic devices for detecting light are continually being developed. Scientists in Australia, for example, are devising an optical fiber so thin (less than $\frac{1}{500}$ inch, or 0.05 millimeters) that it can be used to see right inside the inner ear and repair damage. Other scientists have developed terahertz scanners. Terahertz is a form of radiation with a slightly longer wavelength than infrared light. Terahertz scanners can see right through clothes and show people as if they were naked. Terahertz wands could scan people at airports to make sure they are not carrying hidden weapons.

See also: LIGHT • LIQUID CRYSTAL • MEDICAL IMAGING

Orbit

An orbit is the path taken by an object in space as it moves around another object, held on course by the pull of gravity between them. The movement of a planet like Earth around the Sun is an orbit, as is the path of a spacecraft or the Moon around Earth.

An orbiting space object is called a satellite. Some, like planets' moons, are natural; others, such as the space stations and other unmanned spacecraft that orbit Earth, are artificial satellites.

Orbiting satellites are kept moving by their momentum through space. Just how much momentum a satellite has depends on its mass and speed. The bigger it is and the faster it is moving, the more momentum it has. A satellite orbits at the height above a planet where its momentum exactly balances the pull of gravity between them. If the gravitational pull is greater than the satellite's momentum, it will move in toward the planet. If the satellite's momentum is greater than the gravitational pull, it will fly off into space. The closer to a planet a satellite orbits, the faster it must travel to prevent it from falling toward the planet, because the gravitational pull is very strong. Mercury, the closest planet to the Sun, orbits in just 88 days; Pluto, however, takes almost 250 years.

▼ *Jupiter is so massive compared to its tiny moons that it barely moves in relation to them. The planet stays relatively fixed, while its moons orbit continually at high speeds.*

▲ *This picture shows the International Space Station in orbit around Earth. Space stations and satellites in Earth's orbit actually fall toward Earth, but they move so fast—thousands of miles an hour—that they never drop, following the curve of Earth's surface.*

It seems as if only the satellite is traveling around, while the planet stays fixed in one place relative to it. But this is not quite true; the pull of gravity between satellite and planet is mutual, so the planet moves around, too. In fact, both satellite and planet orbit around the mutual center of gravity of both objects, called the barycenter.

The simplest shape of an orbit is a circle—the path followed by many satellites circling Earth. Most orbits are oval shaped (elliptical), similar to those of the planets around the Sun. When a planet is at its closest to the Sun (the perihelion), it is traveling the fastest. When it is farthest away (the aphelion), the planet is moving at its slowest speed. Some comets have parabolic or hyperbolic orbits, following open curves that will take them out of the solar system. The biggest known orbits are those of galaxies, many of which orbit around the center of galactic clusters with a period of a billion years or more.

Artificial satellite orbits

When launching a satellite to orbit Earth, scientists calculate its speed and trajectory (path) to be sure of placing it in the right orbit. The lower the orbit, the faster the satellite must move to avoid being pulled down by gravity. Most satellites are launched into low Earth orbit, 180 miles (300 kilometers) above the surface, as this orbit needs the least launch energy. To get a satellite into high orbit, over 18,000 miles (30,000 kilometers) up, requires larger rockets. An orbit 22,237 miles (35,786 kilometers) up takes exactly 24 hours. If a satellite in this orbit is over the equator, it stays in the same place above Earth and is said to be geostationary. Many weather and communications satellites have these orbits. Polar orbiting satellites circle Earth from pole to pole about 530 miles (850 kilometers) above the ground. They cover a different strip of Earth's surface each time around, eventually scanning the entire surface in detail.

See also: ASTRONOMY • COMMUNICATIONS SATELLITE • GRAVITY • MASS AND WEIGHT

Organic chemistry

Organic chemistry is the study of the millions of different compounds and molecules that contain carbon. The name *organic* is derived from the fact that scientists once thought that organic chemicals were unique to living organisms. Chemists can now make organic compounds in the laboratory, but organic chemistry has retained its original name.

Carbon is one of the most remarkable of all the chemical elements. It forms millions of different compounds. Amino acids, enzymes, hormones, vitamins, and all the basic chemicals involved in life are organic compounds. So, too, are gasoline, oil, plastics, and many other substances. In fact, nearly 90 percent of all known compounds are organic compounds.

Originally, scientists thought that the chemicals found in living things could be made only by natural processes. Organic chemistry started to become accepted as a separate branch of chemistry when chemists found that they could make organic compounds in the laboratory. In 1828, German chemist Friedrich Wöhler (1800–1882) converted an inorganic compound called ammonium cyanate (NH_4CNO) into urea ($CO(NH_2)_2$), which is an organic substance found in the urine of many animals. Since Wöhler's time, scientists have found many other ways of making organic compounds from both organic and inorganic starter materials. Many important organic chemicals have been created in the laboratory.

▶ *This computer-generated artwork shows the long, ribbonlike structure of a lipase molecule, which is an enzyme involved in the metabolism of fatty substances.*

The unique atom

It is the structure of the carbon atom that makes it such a useful element. Carbon atoms may link together in long chains or ring-shaped structures, forming a range of complex organic compounds. Every carbon atom consists of a central nucleus, around which orbit negatively charged particles called electrons. The electrons orbit in a series of discrete energy levels called electron shells. The way in which the electrons are arranged in the electron shells determines how the carbon atom interacts with other carbon atoms and with the atoms of other elements. Every carbon atom has four

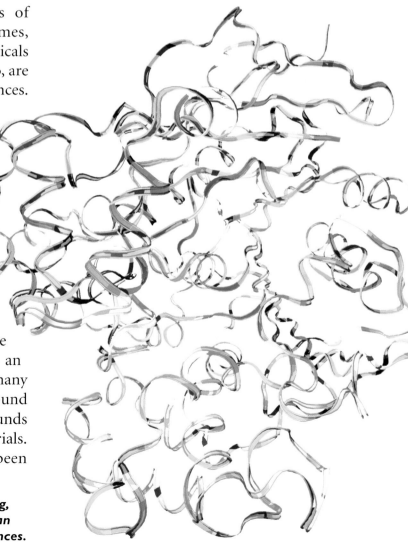

▲ *This computer-generated image shows a molecule of the amino acid alanine ($C_3H_7NO_2$). The color-coded spheres represent atoms of carbon (green), oxygen (pink), nitrogen (blue), and hydrogen (white).*

electrons in its outer electron shell. There is room for eight electrons in this shell, so carbon has four "gaps." These gaps are the key to what makes the carbon atom link so readily with other carbon atoms—the atoms share electrons to fill in the gaps. In this way, carbon can join up in long chains and rings containing hundreds or thousands of atoms.

Many organic compounds consist only of carbon and hydrogen. Called hydrocarbons, they are the simplest organic compounds, with atoms linked together in short, straight chains. However, there are many different ways in which carbon and hydrogen can join up in chains, so there are many

different hydrocarbons. All the world's fossil fuels, such as coal, oil, and natural gas, are hydrocarbons. Fossil fuels are the remains of marine organisms that lived in the oceans millions of years ago. Over time, the remains settled on the seafloor, forming layers of organic sediment. Gradually, a series of chemical and physical changes took place, converting the sediment into fossil fuels. Other organic chemicals contain oxygen as well as carbon and hydrogen. There are many different groups, including alcohols and carboxylic acids.

Polymers

The largest and most complex organic chemicals are called polymers. Some polymers occur naturally. One example is cellulose, which is the fibrous substance in trees and plants. Cotton and wool are natural polymers, too. However, most polymers, including the plastics polyethylene and nylon, are made in the laboratory.

Polymers consist of chains of smaller molecules, called monomers, altered slightly and repeated over again. For example, polyethylene consists of chains of up to 50,000 ethylene monomers. Ethylene is a hydrocarbon with the chemical formula C_2H_4.

Chains and rings

Organic chemicals are often grouped according to the ways in which the atoms are arranged. An aliphatic compound is an organic compound in which the carbon atoms form straight or branched chains. Ethane (C_2H_6), propane (C_3H_8), and paraffin (a mixture of alkanes) are examples of aliphatic compounds. So, too, are hydrocarbons called alkenes, which are the starter materials for the manufacture of many plastics. Another important group of organic chemicals are cyclic compounds, which consist of rings of carbon atoms. Cyclohexane (C_6H_{12}) is a common cyclic compound.

Aromatic compounds are organic compounds that contain a benzene ring. German chemist Friedrich Kekulé von Stradonitz (1829–1896) proposed the currently accepted structure of the benzene ring in 1865. Aromatics get their name from the strong aroma or smell of benzene.

Synthesizing chemicals

One of the most important jobs of the organic chemist is the synthesis of new chemicals. A major breakthrough came in the 1960s with a method known as retrosynthetic analysis. The aim of retrosynthetic analysis is to build up large, complex molecules from cheap, simple molecules.

Retrosynthetic analysis works by picturing the target molecule as if it were a completed jigsaw puzzle. By working backwards, chemists can

▼ **Bicalutamide (sold under the brand name Casodex) is a drug used in the treatment of prostate cancer. Bicalutamide has a similar structure to the male sex hormone testosterone. It blocks testosterone from binding to receptors on the surface of the cancer cells. Without testosterone, the cancer cells either grow more slowly or stop growing altogether.**

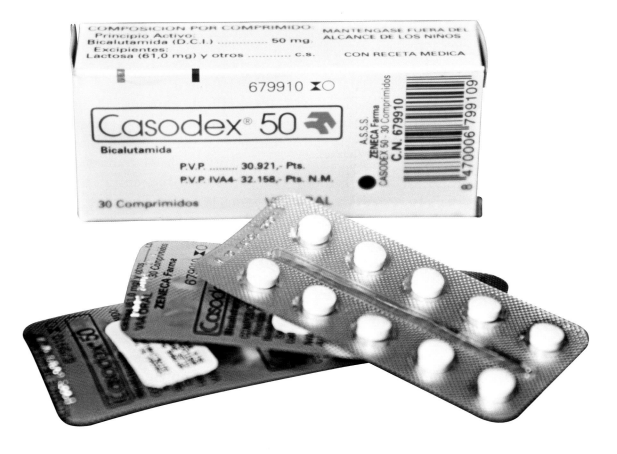

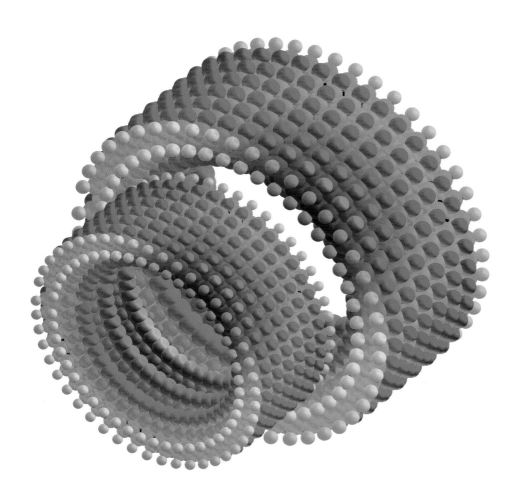

◄ *In this computer model of a molecular bearing, each colored sphere represents a single atom. Complex structures such as this can be constructed using organic compounds.*

determine what types of chemicals are needed to form the complete structure. In this way, they can make anything from a new, environmentally friendly detergent to brighter, safer paints.

An example of retrosynthetic analysis in action is in the manufacture of taxol, which is a drug used to treat certain cancers. Taxol is extracted from the bark of the Pacific yew tree. It consists of three rings of organic molecules to which are attached various chemical groups. To synthesize such a complex chemical will probably take about 25 steps, each using different chemicals. The process may not yield much taxol, but it is such a valuable drug that the retrosynthesis is still worthwhile pursuing.

Using enzymes as catalysts

Using so many steps to convert simple molecules into complex molecules creates problems. Some reactions run so slowly that to speed them up requires very high temperatures and pressures.

Another way to speed up the reactions is to use catalysts. These chemicals speed up the reaction without being used in the reaction themselves. Many are based on precious metals, such as platinum, so they are expensive. They can also be "poisoned" by impurities in the reaction mixtures to which they are exposed.

Organic chemists have turned to nature to help solve the problems. Nature has its own catalysts, called enzymes, which are complex proteins found in all living things. Enzymes have many advantages over manufactured catalysts. For one thing, they often do not need high temperatures. Many also often work with just one type of reaction, which keeps down the number of additional unwanted chemicals that are created. There are more than 10,000 known enzymes, so there is no shortage.

See also: CARBON • CHEMISTRY

Oscilloscope

An oscilloscope is an electronic instrument used by scientists. It can show on its screen how a measured property, such as electrical charge or pressure, changes with time.

Oscilloscopes are widely used in industry, medicine, and scientific research. Medical researchers, for example, use them to study electrical impulses in the brain, while electrical engineers use them to test computers and other electrical equipment.

Oscilloscopes display electrical signals. These signals can come from transducers—devices that convert changes in physical phenomena such as sound, pressure, or vibration into electricity. An oscilloscope displays electrical signals on a screen as thin, bright lines, usually in the form of waves. This allows the input signals to be measured.

Parts of an oscilloscope

An oscilloscope screen is like a conventional television or computer screen, using a cathode ray tube (CRT). Inside the tube is an electron gun, which fires a beam of tiny subatomic particles called electrons at the screen. The electrons produce a fluorescent glow on the screen wherever they strike. There are also two pairs of plates (one pair called X and the other called Y) for steering the beam. The two X-plates bend the beam horizontally across the screen and the Y-plates bend it vertically up and down the screen.

The oscilloscope also has an amplifier, which strengthens the electrical signals going in, and a timebase. The timebase is a sawtooth oscillator, which is connected to the X-plates and controls the horizontal speed of the beam across the screen.

▼ *A microphone picks up the sound vibrations from a tuning fork and converts them into an electrical signal. The signal is displayed as a wavy line on the oscilloscope screen.*

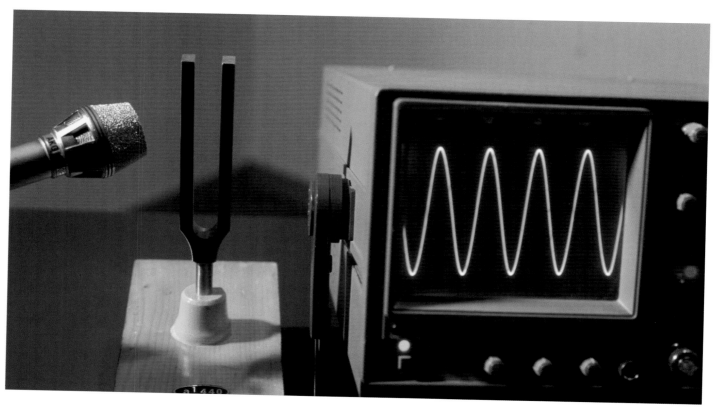

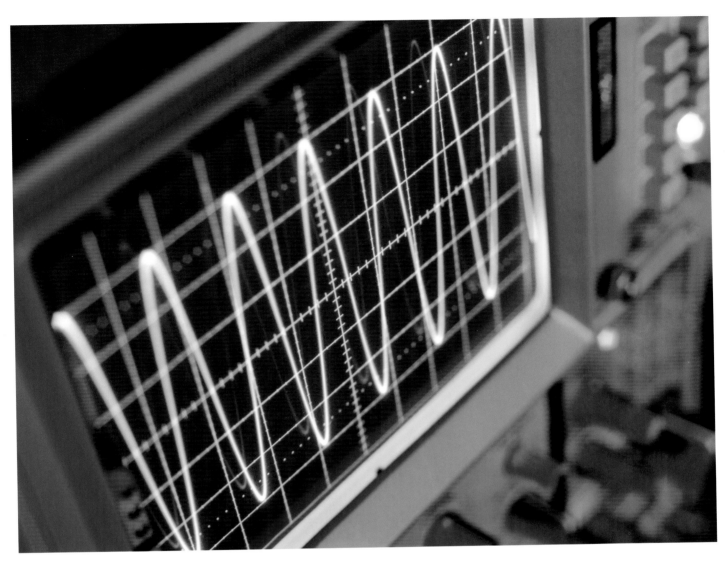

▲ *The oscilloscope displays a regular pulsing signal as a wavy line on the screen. A grid on the screen allows the strength and speed of the signal to be measured and displayed as a graph.*

How oscilloscopes work

First, a fine spot of light is focused on the oscilloscope's screen. The timebase can be set to make the spot sweep across, from left to right, at regular intervals, often just fractions of a second. The spot quickly jumps back to the start after each sweep. The electrical signal is then fed through the amplifier, usually to the Y-plates.

The signal can be moved to any place on the screen by combining the vertical motion (Y) with the horizontal motion controlled by the X-plates. If the signal has a steady pattern or pulse, then the timebase can be set to match it. This process is called synchronization, and it will make the signal appear as regular waves on the display screen.

Additional features

It is possible to show several traces (waves) on one screen by choosing a different vertical position for each signal. To produce more than one trace, the electron beam is split into separate beams. These are controlled by the same timebase circuit and move across the screen together. In this way, they can be compared more easily.

See also: ELECTRON TUBE •
ELECTRONICS • TRANSDUCER

Osmosis

Osmosis is the way in which water containing dissolved chemicals moves through a thin membrane—from where the chemicals are diluted to where they are concentrated. Osmosis is vital for all living things, helping them to maintain the right mix of chemicals and water.

Osmosis is a key function of living cells. It is how cells pump water in from outside. Plants get most of their water by osmosis. In animals, osmosis keeps the balance of water and nutrients between body fluids and body cells. Osmosis is used in industry, too, for tasks such as purifying water and preserving food.

Scientific discovery

The occurrence of osmosis was discovered in 1748 by French physicist Abbé Jean-Antoine Nollet (1700–1770). He covered the bottom end of a glass tube with parchment paper and poured a sugar and water solution into the tube, filling it to a mark on the glass. When the covered end of the tube was placed in a jar of water, the level of the sugar solution in the tube rose.

The level of the solution rose because water molecules were passing through the parchment membrane (a thin wall or skin) into the tube faster

▼ *This osmosis apparatus was used by Scottish chemist Thomas Graham (1805–1869). His osmometer (left) could perform reverse osmosis, by forcing a solution under pressure against a semipermeable membrane at the top of the bell jar.*

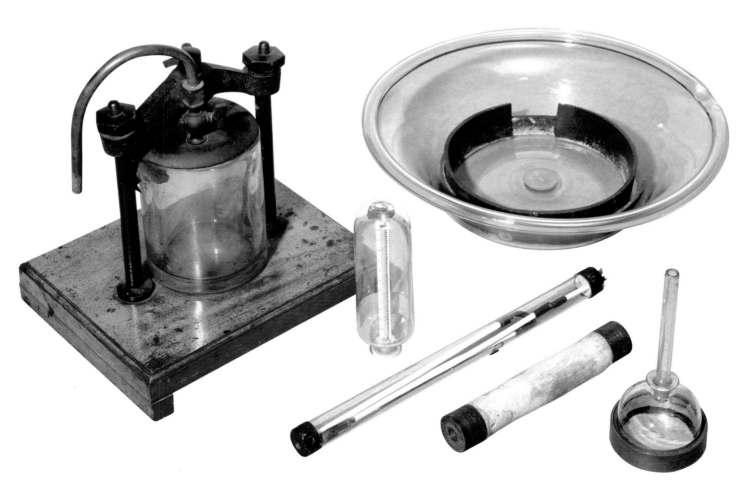

than the sugar molecules could leave the tube through the parchment. Eventually, the sugar solution in the stem fell back to the same level as the water in the jar. The difference at the beginning of the experiment was caused by the fact that water can pass more freely through certain walls than sugar and other solids can.

These walls are described as semipermeable, which means that only substances composed of small molecules, such as liquids and gases, can pass through them. The walls thus let water through freely both ways, but they let through only some of the solid chemicals dissolved within the water.

It is usually the size of the molecules that make up a substance that determines whether it can pass across a semipermeable membrane. Membranes surrounding the cells of the human body and of many animals and plants are semipermeable.

Osmotic pressure

The basis of osmosis is that water tends to pass from a weaker solution to a stronger one if there is the right kind of membrane between them.

A weak, or hypotonic, solution contains proportionally less of the dissolved substance than a strong, or hypertonic, solution does—that is, it contains less of the dissolved substance for a given quantity of water. When osmosis has taken place, the two solutions will be of the same strength. They are then said to be isotonic.

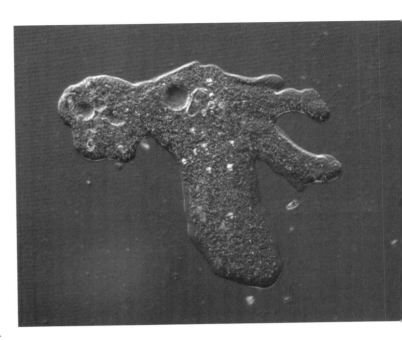

▲ *The amoeba in the picture above is a microscopic, single-celled organism that lives in water. It relies on osmosis to keep the right balance between its body fluid and its surroundings.*

If pure water is sucked into a strong sugar solution, the level of fluid on the sugar side of the wall will rise. At a certain point, there will be so much more water on one side than the other that the pressure it places on the wall will prevent any more water from crossing over. The osmotic pressure can then be measured.

Reverse osmosis

When a pressure greater than the osmotic pressure is applied to a solution, water can be forced back through a semipermeable membrane in the opposite direction. This results in a stronger solution on one side of the membrane, and pure water on the other.

The most popular membrane material for commercial use in reverse osmosis is cellulose acetate, which was first developed for removing salt from seawater. It can also be used for concentrating biological or food material, but it must be chemically sterilized first.

One important use of reverse osmosis is in separating protein from cheese whey. Whey is the watery part of milk, separated from the thicker part

---

DID YOU KNOW?

Shipwreck survivors may owe their lives to osmosis. Normally, osmosis makes water flow from an area of low concentration to one of high concentration—so freshwater flows into seawater when they are separated by a membrane. But, by applying pressure to the seawater, this movement can be reversed in order to make freshwater from seawater. Survival kits often contain the equipment for making drinking water from seawater in this way.

▲ *This is a reverse osmosis desalination equipment in a water plant in Tampa Bay. Using this equipment, the plant changes seawater into drinking water, providing as much as 10 percent of the regional supply.*

during cheese making. The whey is pressed under pressure through a series of tubes lined with cellulose membranes that catch the protein, which can then be spray dried.

Reverse osmosis is sometimes known as ultrafiltration or hyperfiltration, depending on how much solid material is taken from the liquid solution. It is used to produce sugar beet extract, skim milk, various enzymes, and polio vaccines.

Osmosis in the human body
Osmosis is important in helping the blood to circulate freely through our bodies. Osmotic suction keeps the water in the bloodstream from squeezing out into the body tissues. And it constantly balances the amount of water both inside and outside the walls of the blood vessels. Osmosis also keeps the lungs free of fluid and even helps a kidney machine to work, through a process called dialysis.

Osmotic dehydration
Fruits may be preserved by using osmosis and dehydration (water removal) to dry the fruit. Apple slices, for example, are first scalded in boiling water to stop the fruit from spoiling. They are then put into a bath of hot sugar syrup, which is pumped through the bath to maintain the correct osmotic pressure. After four to six hours, nearly half the weight of the fruit has been lost. The water in it has passed into the sugar syrup. The syrup is then washed off, and the apples are dried in a hot oven.

See also: ATOM AND MOLECULE •
CELL • PRESSURE • WATER

Oxidation and reduction

Oxidation and reduction are common chemical reactions, like burning or rusting. These reactions always occur together in what is called a redox reaction. In fact, they are opposite sides of the same reaction. Oxidation is when a substance loses electrons; reduction occurs when it gains electrons.

Oxidation and reduction reactions often involve an exchange of oxygen between substances. As coal burns, for example, the carbon in it joins with oxygen in the air to make carbon dioxide gas (CO_2). Burning, rusting, and corrosion are all common chemical reactions in which a substance combines with oxygen.

Oxidation, therefore, got its name because these common reactions involved substances joining with oxygen—such as the reaction of magnesium with oxygen to form the compound magnesium oxide (MgO). *Reduction* was the name given to a reaction that involves substances parting with oxygen—such as the reaction of copper (I) oxide (CuO) with hydrogen gas (H_2) to form metallic copper and water (H_2O).

One hundred years ago, however, the definition of oxidation and reduction became slightly broader. Scientists realized that when substances were oxidized, their atoms always seemed to give up electrons—the tiny particles that circle the nucleus

▼ *Many statues are cast from bronze, a metal alloy combining copper and tin. In time, the statue turns green, as the copper is oxidized in the air to green copper oxide (Cu_2O).*

of each atom—to form the chemical bond. When substances were reduced—that is, when they lost their oxygen—their atoms gained electrons.

Scientists then realized that substances can lose electrons without any oxygen being involved at all. When a substance loses electrons during oxidation, the lost electrons must always be picked up by another substance. Reduction is the picking up of these lost electrons. The two reactions, therefore, always go together as "redox" reactions.

Oxidation number

For a long time, therefore, oxidation was defined as a loss of electrons, and reduction as a gain of electrons. Then chemists found redox reactions can take place without electrons swapping at all. When carbon dioxide (CO_2) reacts with hydrogen gas, for example, it forms carbon monoxide (CO) and water, without any electrons being transferred. So chemists began to develop the idea of the "oxidation number" or "oxidation state" of each atom in a compound. In carbon dioxide, for example, the oxidation number of carbon is 4, while in carbon monoxide it is 2, oxygen having an oxidation number of –2 in each case. When the oxidation number of one of the atoms in a molecule is lowered, chemists say that the molecule has been reduced. So oxidation is now described as a loss of electrons, or an increase in oxidation number. Reduction is described as a gain of electrons, or a decrease in oxidation number.

Oxidizing and reducing agents

Many substances encourage oxidation reactions, including hydrogen, hydrogen sulfide (H_2S), carbon, carbon monoxide, and sulfurous acid

▼ *Rusting is one of the most common oxidation reactions. Iron exposed to damp air combines with oxygen and water in the air to form brown-red hydrated iron oxide (Fe_2O_3), otherwise known as rust.*

(H_2SO_3). These substances are oxidizing agents and are reduced during the reaction. Many substances encourage reduction reactions, such as halogens, oxygen, ozone (O_3), nitric acid (HNO_3), and sulfuric acid (H_2SO_4). They are called reducing agents and are oxidized during the reaction.

Redox reactions tend to be energetic. Whenever a reaction involves heat or work, it is usually a redox reaction. When natural gas burns, for example, it is an oxidation-reduction reaction that releases a huge amount of heat. Within our bodies, oxidation-reduction reactions are involved in the burning of sugars to release muscle energy.

Rusting and corrosion

One familiar oxidation reaction is the rusting of iron. When iron is exposed to moist air, oxygen in the air combines with water and the iron to form hydrated iron oxide (Fe_2O_3). This is an oxidation reaction, and the iron oxide is the brown-red rust seen on the surface of the iron.

The tarnishing of silver in the air is another oxidation reaction, and so are many other forms of corrosion. Zinc, aluminum, and chromium all turn dark through oxidation when exposed to the air. Unlike rust, however, the dark surface coating does not weaken the metal. Iron is the only metal that really needs to be protected against oxidation—usually by keeping air and water away from it by applying a protective coating such as paint or oil.

Combustion

Another common oxidation-reduction reaction is burning or combustion. Most combustion is basically a very energetic redox reaction releasing heat and light. Combustion can sometimes take place without oxygen—when hydrogen burns in chlorine, for instance. But when fuels such as wood, coal, oil, or natural gas are burned in air, oxygen is always involved. In fact, these substances will not burn unless there is enough oxygen available for the reaction to take place.

▲ *Frothing shows the energetic oxidation of the metal lithium when it is put in water. Oxidation involves a movement of electrons, creating an electric current, and this kind of reaction is the basis of many batteries.*

See also: CHEMICAL REACTION • OXYGEN

Oxygen

Oxygen makes up about one-fifth of the air people breathe. If oxygen were missing for more than a few minutes, we would die. Although life has always needed oxygen, it was not discovered as a separate element until two hundred years ago.

Oxygen is part of Earth's atmosphere. Since it has no smell, taste, or color, however, it is difficult to detect. Of course, people have always known that air is essential to life and that it is needed for fire, but it took longer to discover that it is actually oxygen that plays the vital role. Humans and animals need oxygen to live. They breathe in oxygen from the air (as O_2) and then breathe out carbon dioxide (CO_2) in a process called respiration. Green plants, however, take in carbon dioxide. Using energy from sunlight, they turn carbon dioxide into food by photosynthesis. Oxygen is given off as a by-product, thus completing the "oxygen cycle."

Oxygen is one of the most abundant elements in Earth's crust, waters, and atmosphere. It makes up about one-fifth of the volume of the air, 90 percent of the mass of all water, and 47 percent of the mass of the rocks that make up Earth's crust, although there oxygen is combined with other chemicals, such as silicon, in compounds.

Oxygen is a gas at normal temperatures, and only condenses to a pale blue liquid when the temperature reaches −297°F (−183°C). Oxygen will become liquid at much higher temperatures when under pressure, which is useful since it can be stored in tanks ready for use. At a pressure of 750 pounds per square inch (51 kilograms per square centimeter), it turns to liquid at just −180°F (−118°C).

Oxygen has the chemical symbol "O," and it has an atomic number of eight. Each oxygen atom has two electrons on its inner shell, and six in its outer shell. Since an atom's second shell can normally take eight electrons, this means oxygen has two "gaps." These gaps cause oxygen to readily react with other elements and form compounds. In fact, oxygen is so reactive that it is only found as a pure element in the air—where nitrogen (which makes up most

◀ *All the oxygen in the air comes from plants. Before green plants existed, there was no free oxygen in the air. Plants make oxygen as they use sunlight and carbon dioxide in the air to produce food by photosynthesis.*

◄ *Runners collapse after a race because of oxygen shortage. Muscle power comes from converting blood sugar into energy through a reaction with oxygen—a process called respiration. During strenuous exercise, the muscles can demand so much oxygen that the lungs cannot supply it from the air into the blood fast enough.*

of the rest of air) is so unreactive that even oxygen cannot make it react. Even here, though, oxygen join together in pairs as O_2. Elsewhere, oxygen is involved in many natural chemical reactions called oxidations. Rusting is an oxidation reaction, as is combustion (burning) and respiration.

How oxygen was discovered

English chemist Joseph Priestley (1733–1804) first discovered oxygen. On August 1, 1774, he was watching what strong heat could do to mercuric (II) oxide (HgO). He noticed that it gave off a gas and, to his surprise, a candle would burn in this gas with a strong flame. On a visit to Paris in 1775, he told French chemist Antoine-Laurent Lavoisier (1743–1794) about his discovery. Lavoisier experimented with the new gas and with air. He learned from these experiments that "oxygen," as he named it, was one of the two main gases that make up air (the other being nitrogen). Lavoisier devised a theory of combustion to explain how things burn, and his explanation is still accepted today.

Oxygen in nature

Oxygen is used for many different purposes in nature. Plants need carbon, which they turn into the starches that form their structure. They cannot take in carbon directly from the soil, but they can take it in as part of carbon dioxide from the air. The plant takes out the carbon from the carbon dioxide by photosynthesis, releasing the oxygen that it does not need. Nature uses oxygen as a way of packaging the carbon so that plants can take it in.

Carbon dioxide is poisonous to humans and animals, so plants fulfill a vital role by absorbing it from the air. Humans and animals use oxygen from the air to help them turn sugar from food into energy by respiration. Some oxygen also combines

DID YOU KNOW?

Priestley was experimenting by growing mint underwater when he noticed that bubbles were forming on the leaves. He figured out that plants give off oxygen, and he discovered photosynthesis. The carbon dioxide that humans and animals exhale is, in turn, absorbed by plants, and so an "oxygen cycle" is established. Burning a fuel such as coal involves much the same process. Oxygen is used up (without oxygen, the fire cannot burn), and carbon dioxide and water are produced as waste products.

◀ *Oxygen can be stored in liquid form under pressure in thick metal tanks. Pure oxygen can thus be made available for patients with breathing difficulties, or for divers underwater.*

under pressure. This produces better steel because any impurities are burned out by the fierce heat. Another use is in oxyacetylene torches for cutting and welding metals. As Priestley discovered, flames burn more strongly in oxygen than in air. Thus, a torch burning acetylene gas in a stream of oxygen produces a flame as hot as 6000°F (3300°C) that can cut through metal and even burn underwater.

Oxygen under the sea and in space

Pure oxygen is used, mixed with helium, for deep-sea divers to breathe instead of air. The pressure at depths greater than 250 feet (76 meters) underwater would push nitrogen out of ordinary air straight into a diver's bloodstream, causing the painful condition known as "the bends." Helium is used to dilute the pure oxygen, which on its own would become poisonous after a while.

Most hospitals have piped oxygen supplies that go to various wards and operating rooms in case patients have difficulty breathing. Patients who are

with carbon to make carbon dioxide, which is then exhaled, and some oxygen links up with hydrogen (H_2) to form water (H_2O).

Disadvantages of oxygen

In industry, oxygen is often an expensive nuisance. It causes iron and steel to rust. However, the oxide coating on some metals, such as aluminum and zinc, can protect them from further attack. When oxygen mixes with another substance, they often form a gas, as in the case of carbon. Carbon dioxide is an acidic gas, and so is sulfur dioxide (SO_2)—one of the most destructive gases poured out into the air every day by some industries. Called acid rain, its effect on the environment can be catastrophic.

Oxygen in industry

Oxygen can also be very useful. Its main industrial use is in steelmaking. Instead of blasting air in from the bottom of the furnaces, oxygen is blasted in

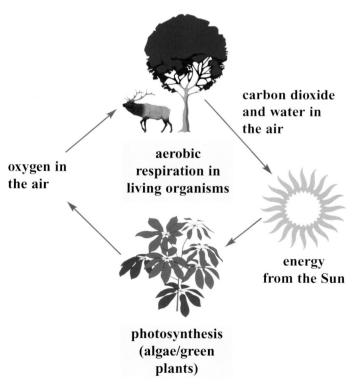

carbon dioxide and water in the air

aerobic respiration in living organisms

oxygen in the air

energy from the Sun

photosynthesis (algae/green plants)

▲ *This diagram shows the oxygen cycle. Oxygen is moved around in a constant cycle between the air and living organisms.*

having breathing problems do much better on pure oxygen than they do on air alone, because of the greater concentration of oxygen that they receive.

Air pressure, and thus the amount of available oxygen, decreases with increasing altitude, so airplane cabins are pressurized to keep the atmospheric pressure nearly normal inside. Airplanes carry an emergency supply of oxygen for passengers to breathe through masks in case the cabin loses normal air pressure while flying.

Oxygen is used as part of the fuel that powers rockets. It is mixed either with kerosene or hydrogen. The two chemicals are stored as liquids and injected at high pressure into the motors, where they mix and burn in the thrust chamber. The gas produced by the controlled explosive reaction goes through specially shaped nozzles at high speed to give the rocket its forward movement.

Ozone

Oxygen atoms are usually found in bound pairs (O_2). When three oxygen atoms bond, the result is ozone gas (O_3). Ozone and oxygen have different properties. Oxygen is vital for breathing, but ozone is poisonous, even at very low concentrations.

Ozone is equally important, however, as it protects Earth from the harmful rays of the Sun. A layer of ozone is formed in the stratosphere (the upper part of Earth's atmosphere) by the action of the Sun on oxygen. The ozone layer absorbs radiation that would be deadly if it could reach us. Scientists warned that chlorofluorocarbons (CFCs), used in aerosol sprays, refrigerators, and industry, were drastically depleting the ozone layer, so the use of CFCs has now been limited.

Making oxygen

There are many ways that oxygen can be made. Water can be split into its two component elements (hydrogen and oxygen) using electricity, by a process called electrolysis. Another method is to heat barium oxide (BaO) in compressed air. It takes an extra oxygen atom from the air and becomes barium peroxide (BaO_2). Cooling the barium peroxide again turns it back into barium oxide, and it gives up the extra oxygen atom as a gas.

Nearly all oxygen is produced by distillation. Air is compressed and cooled to very low temperatures until it becomes a pale blue liquid. Air consists of mostly nitrogen and oxygen, and liquid nitrogen boils at a slightly lower temperature than oxygen. Allowing the liquid air to warm up slowly makes the nitrogen boil off into a gas again, leaving the liquid oxygen behind. This process is called fractional distillation. The nitrogen and oxygen rise to different levels and can be removed separately.

See also: AIR • CHEMISTRY • DISTILLATION • OXIDATION AND REDUCTION • PHOTOSYNTHESIS

Paint

About 20,000 years ago, Stone Age people made paint from natural plant and animal materials. They used it to decorate their caves and color their clothing and their bodies. Many of the hard-wearing and colorful paints now available are made from synthetic materials. These paints are used to protect and decorate homes and furniture.

▲ All the paint colors in the artist's palette are made by adding colored powders or liquids called pigments to an oily substance called a binder. Once applied, the binder quickly evaporates, holding the paint in place.

The first paints were used by prehistoric hunters, who painted pictures of animals on the walls of their caves. Famous examples are at Lascaux in France, and Altamira in Spain. Since then, the basic ingredients of paint have hardly changed. Paint is still made by mixing a colored powder, called a pigment, into a liquid that makes it easy to spread. This liquid is called a medium or binder.

The pigment provides the color and hides the surface of what is being painted. The binder holds all the minute particles of the pigment together, allows them to be spread evenly, and attaches them to the surface. Usually some ingredients in the binder evaporate, leaving a film of the other ingredients and the pigment as a hard layer.

The pigment

Prehistoric people made pigments from natural plant and animal materials, just as some people in developing countries do today. Saffron yellow is made from a crocus, a red pigment comes from the root of the rubia plant, and blue is made from the indigo plant. The early Britons made a blue dye called woad, which they took from a plant of the same name.

Colors could also be made from various rocks and minerals, such as iron oxide, two types of which provided red and yellow. Black was made from soot from fire embers, and white was made from chalk. Different colors could be made by mixing these materials together.

Most pigments are now made by mixing various chemicals together, generally minerals. Compounds of lead, zinc, and barium were widely used for white pigments, but they have now been replaced almost entirely by titanium dioxide. This hides the surface underneath better and is much less poisonous. In fact, the paint industry uses about 65 percent of the world's production of titanium oxide.

In 1972, the U.S. government decided that no household paint should contain more than 0.5 percent of lead. This decision followed incidents in which children were poisoned by consuming flakes of dried paint from toys, walls, and furniture.

DID YOU KNOW?

The scarlet dye color called cochineal is made from the dried bodies of a female insect found in Mexico and Peru. Cochineal is mostly used today as a coloring agent for drinks and cosmetics.

Lead compounds are still used, however, as rust-preventing "primers" that prepare the surface of iron and steel for painting. Lead and the metal chrome go in combination into yellow and orange pigments and are mixed with blue to make green. Other metals used in making pigments are cadmium, for making a yellow color, and copper, which goes into blue.

The binder

The liquid that "carries" the pigment can be almost any substance that dries out. Many liquids have been tried and used successfully. The earliest cave painters used substances like animal blood or fat and beeswax to carry their pigments. Later artists mixed their pigments with water (for watercolors), egg yolk, or wax. But the great breakthrough in art came with the development of oil as a binder. Oil was probably first used in the fourteenth century by Flemish painter Jan van Eyck (1390–1441). Using oil, he was able to paint small pictures with extraordinary precision. Since van Eyck's day, artists (and the makers of household paints) have almost always used oils of some kind as the binder for their pigments.

The traditional oil in paint binder has been linseed oil. Turpentine is used as a thinner so that the paint can be spread easily on the painting surface. Other substances are added to help the binder dry more quickly. A binder of linseed oil alone might take days or even weeks to dry completely. This would be very inconvenient if several coats of paint were being applied.

Mixing a natural resin with the oil helped to improve the spreading qualities, the rate of drying, and the final gloss of the surface. This blend of oil and resin became known as varnish and, with more development, led to longer-lasting enamel and hard high-gloss paints.

Soybean oil is a widely used substitute for linseed oil. This oil makes a binder that is less likely to turn yellow with age and thus is useful for white and pale colors. Other oils that do not turn yellow are sometimes used. They are mainly extracted from

◀ **Shown are two of the most commonly used paint pigments. The black powder is ilmenite, a natural mineral. The white powder is titanium dioxide. Titanium oxide is widely used because it is less poisonous than lead or barium, which were used in the past.**

the seeds of such plants as tobacco, safflower, sunflower, and poppy. Poppy oil is often used for artists' oil colors.

Modern binders

Binders (and pigments) now contain many artificial chemicals. The popular emulsion paints are often made with a kind of plastic resin mixed with water. Developments in plastics technology has given the paint industry several other new resins to replace the old natural ones.

Paint for the artist

Although paint sounds simple enough to make—basically a powder pigment mixed into a liquid binder—to make a large quantity and to ensure that each drop is exactly the same in color and thickness is a very difficult job.

Artists, who used to have to make their own paints, only needed to make enough paint for the size of the canvas. Even at the time of van Eyck, this was not a big task, though it was quite laborious.

First, the artist would have collected the various pigments that would be needed for the painting. This would not mean a separate pigment for each tiny patch of color, because artists could mix paint as they went along to produce all the different shades and tints they needed. They would probably start out by making a dozen basic colors.

Next, the artist would have ground the pigment powders as finely and as evenly as possible, with all the grains the same size and with no lumps. This

▼ *Most paint pigments are now made using colors from artificial minerals. Yellow pigment used to be made from the poisonous cadmium compound. It is now made from a harmless mineral called arylide.*

▶ *Workers in the British Airways paint hangar are preparing the tail fin of a Boeing 747–400 airliner with new livery. Paint provides protection to the fuselage and serves as a way to identify the aircraft.*

would probably be done with a pestle and mortar, working on the same pigment several times, and sifting in between. Then the pigment would have to be stirred into the binder, which had been mixed beforehand. Thinners would be added until the consistency was about right, and the entire batch would be stirred and stirred again. One way to do the stirring was to use a type of mill consisting of two glass plates or stones, like a tiny version of a mill for grinding flour. It would not matter if the color was not precisely the same as it had turned out last time, or if the paint was somewhat too thick. Both could be adjusted as the artist painted.

Paint manufacture

In contrast to the making of artists' paints, the modern manufacturer of household paint cannot afford to sell one can of a particular colored paint that is even slightly different from all the others. Color especially must be absolutely the same, and the consistency has to be within very close limits.

First, the pigments are finely ground by machine and sifted. The pigments are then milled with the binder between rollers that turn at different speeds. The paint is squeezed and rubbed by the rollers, and the different speeds give a more evenly spread film of paint. When it is ready, the paint is taken off the front roller with a scraper blade. Another method is the ball mill, in which a rotating cylinder is half filled with steel or porcelain balls. Paint is added until the cylinder is about three-quarters full, and then the mill is turned for 16 hours.

A development of the ball mill is the sand mill, in which sand or very fine glass beads are driven through the mill with the paint at high speed. The paint finally comes out through a fine strainer that holds back the sand. This allows paint to be made continuously instead of in batches.

The color and consistency of the paint are monitored throughout the process. It is then finally checked and tested before packaging.

Applying paint

Paint can be applied by a brush or roller, by dipping or by spraying. Recently, another way has been used: electropainting. This method works only with metal objects because it relies on electricity. Electropainting is now very widely used in the automobile industry because it paints the entire car in just a few minutes, and it ensures that there are a minimum of gaps in the paint where corrosion could start. The car body is connected to an electric current, then dipped in a big tank of paint. The electric charge on the car attracts the paint. After just a few minutes, the paint can be lifted from the bath, blow dried, and baked to harden the paint.

See also: DYE AND DYEING • PRINTING

Paper and papermaking

Paper is a vital part of the modern world, used for everything from packaging to making magazines, books, and newspapers. Every year, the world makes over 350 million tons (318 million tonnes) of paper. Almost one third of this is made in the United States.

There are many different kinds of paper, but all are made from plant fibers made of cellulose. The fibers are mixed with water, then filtered through a fine screen so that they mat together into a sheet. Chemical bonds form between the cellulose molecules as the sheet dries, so that the paper forms a light, surprisingly strong material.

Paper is made from a wide variety of different plants, from pine trees to rice. Indeed, paper can actually be made from almost any plant. For hundreds of years, plant fibers came mainly from pulped cotton and linen rags, but in the last century, most paper has been made from wood pulp, mostly from conifers such as pines and firs. Cotton rags are still used for high-quality paper.

The invention of paper

The word *paper* comes from *papyrus*, a reed that the ancient Egyptians used for making writing materials over four thousand years ago. The papyrus reed grew widely in the Nile Delta. The Egyptians cut the stem of papyrus in triangular sections, which could be easily peeled into strips. They laid these strips edge to edge on a flat surface, put a second layer crosswise over them, and then beat them with a heavy mallet to flatten them and make the fibers stick together. After drying in the sun, the treated papyrus became sheets of writing material. The sheets were joined edge to edge to make scrolls that could be rolled up for storage.

Paper as we know it was invented by the Chinese about two thousand years ago. Legend has it that Ts'ai Lun, an official attached to the Chinese imperial court, discovered how to make paper from the bark of the mulberry tree. He mixed the fibers with water to form a pulp, and shook it through a fine sieve until an even layer formed on the top of the sieve. When drained, this layer formed a sheet. It was carefully removed and smoothed out against a wall to dry in the sun. Later, the Chinese found that they could make paper fibers by beating rags,

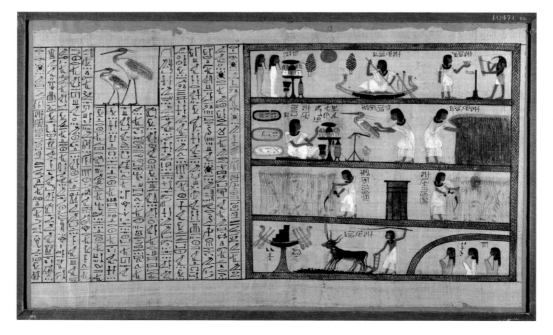

◀ *Ancient Egyptian scribes wrote on a material called papyrus, which was made from strips of a dried reed. It was this material that gave us the word* paper. *Papyrus is so strong that ancient Egyptian scrolls have survived more than four thousand years.*

▶ *The papermaking process begins in forest plantations such as this one, where coniferous trees such as pine, fir, and spruce are felled and cut into the logs that will be used to make wood pulp.*

rope, or old fishing nets to a pulp. The paper they made was too coarse for writing, but they used it for wrapping and painting.

In the eighth century, the Arabs captured some Chinese papermakers in what is now Turkestan, and persuaded them to carry on their craft in Samarkand. In 795 CE, the Arabs started their own papermaking industry in Baghdad. Papermaking eventually spread to Europe following the Crusades and the Arab conquest of Spain.

Parchment and vellum

Until then, most documents in Europe had been written on parchment, made from the skin of sheep or goats, or on vellum, which is made from the skin of a calf. Parchment and vellum were tough and long lasting, but took a long time to make, and were only available in limited quantities. It has been estimated that a single book two hundred pages long would have needed the skins of 12 sheep.

The process for making parchment was much like leather making. Parchment was cut into rectangles and then joined at the edges to make scrolls. Then, about two thousand years ago, a better way was found of storing it. Each rectangle was folded once, twice, or three times, and the folds were cut to make separate sheets. These sheets were called folio (which gave two pieces from one fold), quarto (four pieces from two folds), and octavo (eight pieces from three folds). They became the page sizes used for many years afterward. The parchment pages were stored by binding them between thin flat wooden boards—the world's first books.

Rags, rolls, and wood

By the time German printer Johannes Gutenberg (1400–1468) invented movable type for printing in the 1450s, paper had largely replaced parchment as the main writing material. Paper was made mainly from old rags boiled together, beaten, then stirred into a large amount of water, which made a pulp. A

thin layer was removed from the top of the watery pulp by dipping a sieve in and moving it across the surface. This thin layer was then pressed flat, then hung out to dry on wooden poles.

Papermaking changed little until the Industrial Revolution, when the demand for paper spurred two major developments. First, in 1798, French inventor Nicholas-Louis Robert (1761–1828) devised a machine for making paper in continuous rolls. This labor-saving machine was refined by English brothers Henry Fourdrinier (1766–1854) and Sealy Fourdrinier (1774–1847), and it remains the model for papermaking machines.

Then, in the 1840s, a way was found of making paper not from rags but from wood pulp. This was the "stone-ground wood" method, invented in Germany. U.S. chemist Benjamin Tilghman (1821–1901) found a way to quickly soften the wood fibers using sulfurous acid (H_2SO_3), and in 1883, German chemist Carl Dahl found that by adding sodium sulfate (Na_2SO_4), he could make a very strong pulp. Dahl's process, called the *kraft* process (from the German word meaning "strength") remains the main papermaking process.

The kraft process and Fourdrinier machines are still the main methods used to make paper, but modern papermaking machines are now often

◀ *Paper mills process vast quantities of softwood logs, which are crushed and chemically treated to make pulp. Most of the world's softwood production ends up in paper.*

computer controlled, and many refinements have been introduced to speed and improve the process and reduce pollution.

Materials for paper

Rags are used to make handmade and high-quality paper. Flax, jute, grasses, and seed fibers are used for the cheapest, low-quality paper. The most widely used material, however, is wood pulp. Wood for paper is either harvested for this purpose or comes from lumber wastes. Synthetic (artificial) materials have been tried, but so far they have not worked well or they are too expensive. Increasingly, however, old paper is recycled. For every ton of waste paper collected and recycled for new paper, at least two trees are saved.

The first part of paper manufacture is to make a pulp. This is done in two ways, depending on the quality of paper to be made. The mechanical method is used for paper that is not of high quality and that will not last long. Newsprint, which is used for all our newspapers, is an example of this kind. The chemical method is used for paper of better quality, such as writing paper.

Mechanical pulpmaking

The mechanical method is used for making pulp from soft wood, such as that from conifers. Logs from the trees are trimmed by machines and stripped of their bark. Then they are ground into small fibers, usually by rotating saws, and these are flushed away with water.

The solution of fibers and water is then screened. That is, it is passed through screens to remove some of the impurities and lumps. This process is something like putting flour through a sifter to make it finer for baking cakes. The larger lumps in the pulp are then screened again or burned.

If the pulp is to be sent from the pulp mill to a paper mill elsewhere, it is pressed into sheets. If the pulp is being processed further at the same mill, it will then go to a machine called a concentrator, and some of the excess water will be removed. The pulp can be made air-dry, which means that it has 10 percent moisture left. It can also be made wet, or moist, which means that it has 45 percent moisture. The fibers of air-dry pulp are so weak that they have to be mixed with from 15 to 50 percent of pulp made by the chemical method.

Chemical pulp making

The chemical method of making pulp involves cooking. It removes more of the impurities from the raw material, which means that the amount of pulp will be less but the quality higher. Two kinds of chemicals are used. In papermaking terms, one is called an acid liquor and the other one an alkaline liquor.

Acid liquor is usually bisulfate with a little sulfur dioxide gas added. This is used mostly for spruce, which is the most common source of wood for paper in North America. Logs are made ready for acid liquor pulping by being sliced and then broken into chips. These chips are screened until they are about ¼ to ¾ inch (0.5 to 2 centimeters) in size. Then they are pressure cooked in a machine called a digester, which is heated by steam. The quality of the pulp is affected by the size of the chips, the strength of the acid, the level of pressure applied, and the cooking time.

After the cooking process, some of the sulfur dioxide can be recovered. This waste liquor can then be used as a tanning agent in leather manufacture to remove any lime that is still present in the animal skins. However, the use of acid liquor can create a serious pollution problem.

There are several kinds of alkaline liquor, and these are used for non-wood fibers such as rags and straw, and for hardwood. Before the pulping, rags must be sorted and straw must be chopped and cleaned of dust. Softwoods with a large amount of resin in them, such as pine, can also be pulped chemically because alkalines dissolve resin.

The different alkalines

Sodium hydroxide (caustic soda) is one of the substances used in alkaline liquor. One of its benefits is that when used on wood, about 85 percent of the soda can be recovered from the waste liquor for reuse. Sodium sulfate is another of the alkaline liquors used in the kraft process. It changes into sodium sulfide in the digester, and this substance helps the fibers keep their strength. Another benefit of the kraft process is that the scum formed on the waste liquor can be used for soap and lubricant (oil) manufacture. However, its great

◀ *These workers in a paper mill are checking the quality of the wood pulp before it goes on to be made into the finished paper.*

disadvantage is that the kraft process is extremely smelly. Sodium monosulfite is among the newer chemicals used for cooking pulp in alkaline liquor. It is also called neutral sulfite. The advantage of neutral sulfite is that it will work on hardwoods that could not be used for making paper before.

Cleaning the pulp

After the pulp has been made, it must be treated to get rid of the remaining impurities. This is basically a washing, but sometimes bleaching is also needed. Some pulps can be washed while still in the digester, but usually they are removed at once so the digester can be used again. In the past, impurities were slowly removed with filtration screens, but filters have now been replaced by centrifugal and vortex cleaners, which rely on whirling the pulp around at high speeds to fling out the impurities.

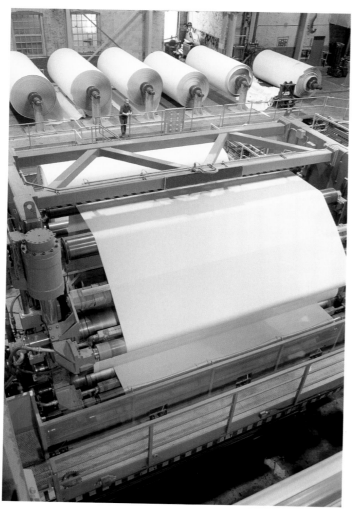

One of the impurities that is removed is lignin, a natural substance found in all fiber. Lignin makes fibers turn yellow in light. Cheap paper, which is not cleaned as well as more expensive paper, therefore turns yellow faster.

Beating

If the pulp comes to the paper mill in sheet form, it must be ground up again. This time it is done in a machine called a hydrapulper, which is shaped like a large cask. The hydrapulper breaks down the sheets in water (*hydra* comes from the Greek word for water). If waste paper is being used, it must also go through a treatment like this. The use of waste paper is increasing, too, because of the need to preserve the world's trees, and because the price of pulp has become so high.

The next step is beating, which is very important to the final quality of the paper. Beating affects the length of the fibers (shorter fibers are stronger), their plasticity (ability to change and keep their shape), and their ability to bond (stick together) in the paper machine. These, in turn, affect the finished paper's strength, bulk, and opacity. Opacity—the ability of a substance to block light—is used as a measure of paper thickness.

Hollanders and refiners

The most widely used beating machine is the hollander, so called because it was introduced from Holland in the eighteenth century. The hollander is an oval tube with a low ridge across the center from side to side. This wall actually falls short of the sides, however, so that the pulp can flow around it. On one side there is a roll with bars on it, mounted on a shaft. This is called the beater roll. The pulp, which is now called stock or stuff, is ground against some bars on the floor as well as the beater roll.

This traditional machine is still used for handmade paper, but has been replaced by the refiner for cheaper paper, especially newsprint. The

◀ *This stack of heavy steel rollers is called a calendar. Once paper has been made, it is usually run through a calendar to smooth it. This process makes the paper suitable for writing and printing.*

From pulp to paper

Now the stock is ready to go into the actual paper-making machine. The one in most general use is called the Fourdrinier. The original Fourdrinier machines did not do the finishing, which was done by hand, but today these machines do the entire job in one continuous process. The stock goes in at the wet end and comes out as dry, finished paper.

The stock is first poured continuously onto a moving belt called the cloth (even though it is made of wire or plastic mesh like screens). The machine gives the cloth a short shake sideways as the stock comes onto it, which helps the fibers mesh better. As the water drains off the stock through the mesh, the fibers stick together tightly to form what is called a web. Suction is applied by means of vacuum boxes under the cloth. This will remove more of the water. At the same time, a lightweight wire-covered roller, called a dandy roll, moves along the top surface and presses the web.

As the web moves along, it is separated from the cloth by a pair of rollers (on older machines) and by a single suction roll (on newer ones). These are called couch rolls. The web is then laid on a bed of felt and is carried farther along between two pressure rolls. This removes more water so that, at this stage, 65 percent of the water is gone. The web next passes into the dry end of the machine. It then goes around a series of paired iron cylinders (large tubes) heated by steam. This is called the drying train. By now the web is paper. But it has been overdried and is without a surface finish.

The finishing comes next, as the paper passes through several pairs of highly polished iron pressure rolls. These are called calendar stacks, and they smooth the surface finish of the paper. Next the paper passes over sweat rolls, which put some of the moisture back to correct the overdrying. Finally, the paper is wound onto large reels. If it is to be packed on other reels, it is simply slit to the right width. If it is to be used in sheet form, it is cut to size on a cutting machine.

▲ *A worker in a paper mill storage room stacks large rolls of paper ready for delivery. These large rolls will be purchased by commercial paper suppliers, who cut and package the paper for different uses.*

refiner looks much like the hollander, but its beater roll is shaped like a cone. This roller also runs faster, reaching 3,000 feet (over 900 meters) per minute.

It is during the beating or refining process that sizing agents, fillers, and pigments or dyes are added. Sizing helps keep the paper from getting soaked through by water, so that water-based inks will not spread when used on it.

Newsprint does not need sizing because printing ink is oil-based. Fillers are added to improve the paper's opacity, so that writing or printing will not show through from one side to the other. All these materials are white and include china clay, chalk, and titanium oxide.

See also: FIBER • PRINTING • TIMBER INDUSTRY

Parachute

A parachute is a large, umbrella-shaped device designed to allow a person or object to fall safely from a great height. The parachute prevents gravity from pulling the person or object down to the ground too quickly by increasing the air resistance, or drag, around the falling object.

Most parachutes are used for sport by skydivers, but they are also used to drop troops into enemy territory, for rescue missions, and for dropping supplies into remote areas far from roads or rivers. Huge parachutes are also used to slow space shuttles as they land at extremely high speeds; a smaller parachute, called a drogue, pulls out the main parachute. Smaller parachutes are used in the same way by military airplanes landing on short runways.

The first parachutes

The Chinese are believed to have thought of the idea of the parachute about one thousand years ago. In 1483, Italian architect, artist, and scientist Leonardo da Vinci (1452–1519) drew a detailed diagram of a parachute. However, it was not until the 1780s, about the same time as the balloon was invented, that the first known parachute jumps were made. Although French aeronaut Louis-Sébastien Lenormand (1757–1839) made a successful jump with two umbrellas from a tower in 1783, the first parachute jump from a balloon was made by French aeronaut André-Jacques Garnerin (1769–1823) in 1797. Garnerin went on to demonstrate his parachute by making parachute jumps all over Europe from heights of up to 8,000 feet (2,400 meters).

These first parachutes were made of cotton. Unlike modern parachutes, these early designs were constructed around rigid bamboo frames. It was

▲ *Paratroopers are a key part of any modern army. Parachutes are an effective way of deploying troops into the heart of enemy territory. Jumping in full combat gear requires long training.*

only in the late 1800s that soft, silk parachutes that folded in a bag were used; it was not until the early 1900s that parachutists first used a rip cord to pull the parachute quickly from the bag after he or she jumped. This was about the time, in 1912, that Captain Albert Berry of the U.S. Army made the first successful parachute jump from an airplane.

Troop drops and ejector seats

By World War II (1939–1945), the design of parachutes had improved so much that they were regularly used to drop troops and supplies from airplanes, even behind enemy lines. Later, when jet airplanes were introduced, a new type of parachute was developed. A pilot or crew member could eject, seat and all, from the airplane, and the parachute would open automatically at a safe distance from the moving airplane. Modern parachutes come in many different designs, serving many purposes.

The canopy

Parachutes work very simply by using a large surface area to increase the air resistance, or drag, of a falling object. The larger the surface area of the parachute, the more air resistance it creates, and the greater the drag. Parachutes designed for skydiving are between 24 and 28 feet (7 and 9 meters) across when fully opened. Parachutes designed to drop vehicles or crates of supplies are much bigger, often up to 100 feet (30 meters) across.

The part of the parachute that catches air is called the canopy and is typically made of very light nylon. Early parachutes were shaped like an umbrella, and large cargo parachutes are still this shape. However, most skydivers now use rectangular parachutes—typically 11 feet (3.4 meters) deep and 22 feet (6.8 meters) wide. The front of the canopy is cut off, allowing air to enter and inflate the parachute. The rectangular design allows much greater control over the speed and direction of the descent—allowing skilled skydivers to perform aerobatics, and to steer themselves down accurately to a chosen landing spot.

Parachute design

Parachute canopies consist of sections called gores, which are pieces of fabric that are sewn together. A canopy may be either flat or shaped, and this depends on the design and shape of the gores. As its name suggests, a flat canopy can be laid out flat. A shaped canopy will assume its proper shape when it

▲ *Modern rectangular parachutes work in a similar way to an airplane's wing. Skilled skydivers have great control over their parachutes, steering them toward the ground with precise tugs on the steering lines.*

◄ **Parachutes are folded to fit into the pack neatly but open quickly at the right angle and inflate immediately with no snags when the ripcord is pulled.**

of the parachute opening. The harness also has quick-release hooks so the parachutist can escape from the parachute in case the landing is in water or high wind, preventing the injuries that can occur when a parachute drags a skydiver along the ground.

Skydiving

Skydivers always carry two parachutes. The large main parachute is designed for a normal jump. On the top of the pack, there is a smaller reserve parachute, in case the main parachute fails to open.

Skydivers rarely open the parachute immediately after they jump out of an airplane. Typically, they "free-fall" for some time. Some will jump from an altitude of up to 15,000 feet (4,600 meters) and fall at speeds of more than 100 miles (160 kilometers) per hour. Skydivers normally open their parachutes at about 2,500 feet (750 meters) above the ground. As the parachute opens, it immediately slows the descent. By the time they reach the ground, the skydivers are falling at no more than 20 miles (32 kilometers) per hour.

To open the parachute, a skydiver first pulls the ring on his or her leg strap. This pulls out the pin that holds the flaps shut on the pack and makes the small "pilot" parachute folded between the flaps spring out. The pilot parachute quickly inflates and pulls the main parachute out of the pack.

With a rectangular parachute, the skydiver has tremendous control over the direction of his or her descent. By pulling on the right-hand steering line, a skydiver can stop air from entering the right side of the canopy. As the canopy deflates, it falls slightly faster, twisting the skydiver to the right. By pulling on the left-hand steering line, the skydiver can twist to the left. As the skydiver moves toward land, he or she can pull down hard on the rear edge of the parachute to slow the descent even more and give a controlled, soft landing.

is inflated. Inflated canopies usually take the form of a bell shape or a pyramid, but there are many other possibilities.

Garnerin's original parachute was flat and circular and consisted of triangular gores. It also had a vent at the center to allow air to escape. This prevented the parachute from being flung about violently by air forcing its way out from the parachute's underside.

Modern parachutes consist of more than twenty gores, each comprising several smaller panels. They are cut and sewn on the bias (diagonally across the fabric) to give the canopy extra strength. Any tears that may open up will run toward the strong, main seams joining the gores and not spread any further.

The pack

A skydiver's parachute is folded into a thick nylon pack, which is held shut by rip cord pins. The pack is attached to the skydiver with a harness of straps that fit around the legs and shoulders. The harness is designed to prevent injury to the parachutist when the free fall is violently interrupted by the shock

See also: AIRPLANE • BALLOON • GRAVITY

Parasitology

Parasitology is the study of parasites. Parasitic organisms enter the bodies of other organisms and feed off them, causing great harm. Some of the world's worst diseases are caused by parasites. They are often carried by insects whose bite can pass on the parasite responsible for the disease.

When plants or animals of two different species live in close association with each other, their relationship is called a symbiosis. In many cases, both partners in the symbiosis benefit from the relationship. In a few cases, only one will get any benefit, but the other is not affected at all. However, many relationships involve one partner benefiting from the relationship by causing damage to the other partner. This is called a parasitic relationship. The organism causing the damage is called a parasite, and its partner is called the host. Parasites spend all or part of their lives living on or inside the host. Fleas, tapeworms, and mistletoe are examples of parasitic organisms.

A parasite does not kill its host, because it cannot survive without it and will have to find a new host to live in. However, a host eventually becomes weakened by the parasite, and this makes it vulnerable to attack in other ways.

Studying parasites

Parasitology is the study of parasites. It is important to study them because many of the most dangerous human diseases are caused or spread by parasites.

Parasitology also investigates parasitoids. These are a group of animals that live like parasites for some of their life, but they always eventually kill their hosts. For example, many wasp species are

▶ *This mosquito is an ectoparasite of humans that feeds on blood. As it feeds, the mosquito passes on the virus that causes yellow fever.*

parasitoids. The adult female wasps lay their eggs inside the body of a living host, generally another insect. Once hatched, the young insects, called larvae (*singular*, larva) remain inside the host like a parasite, slowly eating its insides and eventually killing it. Then the wasp larvae turn into adults themselves and fly away in search of hosts within which to lay their eggs.

Parasite life cycles

Most animal parasites and parasitoids are insects and worms. Parasites that live on the outside of the body, such as mites (tiny relatives of spiders), are called ectoparasites. Those that live inside the body, such as flatworms (flukes and tapeworms) and nematodes (roundworms) are called endoparasites. Most animal parasites are relatively small, even microscopic, but a few can grow to be very large. Tapeworms may grow as long as 10 feet (3 meters).

Parasites need a way to get from one host to another. Sometimes the eggs or larvae are left in places where they stand a chance of being picked up by the host. For example, chickens pick up the eggs of nematode worms when feeding. The worms grow inside the bird, and more eggs pass out in the chicken droppings. Other parasites need "vectors" to move from host to host. Vectors are other animals that carry the parasite but are not

themselves affected by it. A classic example of a vector at work is the mosquito. Mosquitoes are small flies that are themselves parasites, sucking blood from mammals. Several species of mosquitoes carry other microscopic parasites, such as the protozoans that cause malaria or the viruses that cause dengue fever or yellow fever.

The life cycles of many parasites are complex. For example, gall wasps, which attack oak trees, begin their cycle in late summer, when females lay their eggs on the undersides of leaves. The egg develops into a larva, feeding on the plant tissue. The larva pupates, and in spring a wasp emerges, quite different in appearance from its parent. This wasp never mates. It flies to the newly opening tassels of oak flowers and lays eggs inside. From these eggs hatch males and females that will mate on the wing. Then the females lay their eggs in late summer, and the cycle starts all over again.

Parasitic diseases

Parasitic diseases are the highest single cause of illness in the world today. Every year, one million people die of malaria alone, which is a parasitic disease carried by mosquitoes. In total, 400 million people are infected with parasites.

These diseases can cripple, blind, and eventually kill their victims. They also weaken the body's defenses against other diseases.

As well as malaria, parasitic diseases include river blindness, which is caused by worms, and sleeping sickness, which is caused by a single-celled flagellate carried by the blood-sucking African tsetse (pronouced set-sē) flies. Elephantiasis is caused by parasitic worms that produces huge swellings of the body. A person suffering from the disease hookworm may have five thousand or more worms in his or her body, each one producing tens of thousands of eggs per day. Worldwide, it is estimated that hookworms drink several million gallons of human blood every day of the year.

Parasitic diseases are on the increase. They occur mostly in developing tropical countries in Africa, Asia, and Central and South America, where there is not enough money to pay for the best drugs and vaccines needed to fight them. There is also the possibility that they can spread to other countries, either through travel or imported food.

Malaria

The malaria parasite is carried by the *Anopheles* mosquito, which breeds in swamps, puddles, and stagnant (still water) pools. The mosquitoes become carriers by biting a person who already has malaria. The parasite then grows inside the mosquito and is passed from person to person when the mosquito bites. While the parasite is in the mosquito, it does not cause malaria.

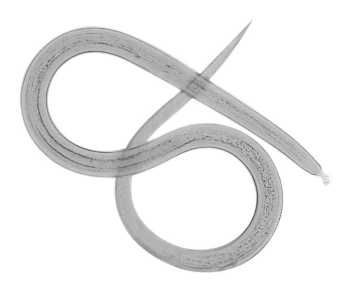

▲ **Hookworms live in the intestines and are among the most common human parasites. Infected people may suffer from anemia, fever, and itching. If the worms reach the lungs, they cause a cough.**

◀ **This blood fluke is a flatworm that lives in the blood. The blood fluke has a mouth but no rear opening to its gut. A sucker on its underside helps the parasite cling to the walls of large blood vessels.**

▶ *This parasitic wasp is laying eggs inside a gypsy moth caterpillar. When the eggs hatch, the larvae feed on the insides of the caterpillar and will eventually kill it. Parasitic wasps are often used in pest control.*

In 1955, the World Health Organization (WHO) launched a worldwide attack against malaria. They drained the swamps where the mosquitoes bred, or sprayed them with oils, to kill the mosquito larvae. They sprayed houses in affected areas with insecticides (chemicals that kill insects) and gave drugs to people who were at risk of catching malaria.

At first, this was very effective. Malaria was eliminated from Europe, large parts of Russia, the United States, Japan, Australia, the West Indies, and Taiwan. By 1961, the number of malaria cases in India and Pakistan had fallen from tens of millions each year to as few as 50,000.

Gradually, however, the mosquitoes developed a resistance to the insecticides, and the drug treatment also became less effective. The use of insecticides was criticized as being unsafe after farmers found that the chemicals stayed in the soil for a long time. These problems caused the goal of the antimalaria campaign to change, from trying to eliminate the disease to preventing its spread. As a result, the number of people suffering from malaria worldwide has increased again.

River blindness

Another serious parasitic disease is onchocerciasis (river blindness). This disease is caused by a worm that enters the human body through the bite of the

DID YOU KNOW?

The larvae of the guinea worm live inside a water flea found in stagnant ponds in the tropics. When people drink the water, the fleas are digested in the stomach, but the larvae survive and grow into worms up to 3 feet (1 meter) long. The best way to fight the disease is to use simple nylon cloth filters that remove the larvae from drinking water.

female black fly. The black fly lives in fast-flowing water and is found in many parts of Africa, Central and South America, and Asia.

The adult worms can grow to a length of 20 inches (50 centimeters). They live coiled up beneath the skin, and each one produces thousands of tiny larvae. The larvae reinfect the black fly when it bites an infected person. The larvae stay beneath the skin while they grow into adults, but they also gather in the eye, causing blindness, which gives this disease its common name.

In the Volta Basin in West Africa, ten million people are exposed to the disease, and one million are infected. Of these, 100,000 are totally blind. Furthermore, some of the best land for growing crops, where there is plenty of water, has been abandoned because of the black fly.

There is no cure for the disease, and so far no vaccine has been developed to prevent infection. The main hope is to reduce the number of black flies. However, this is not easy in areas as large as the Volta, and the black flies themselves are not easy to eliminate. They can travel about 90 miles (150 kilometers) a day, carried by the breeze.

Nevertheless, some progress has been made by spraying an insecticide on the black fly's breeding grounds. Millions of tons of insecticide have been

▲ *A fungal fruiting body grows from a tree trunk. The fungus is the parasite; the tree is the host. The main body of the fungus grows inside the tree itself.*

dropped in the Volta Basin since the project started in 1975. Since then, the spread of river blindness has fallen only slightly.

Schistosomiasis

Schistosomiasis (or bilharzia) affects 200 million people worldwide. This disease is caused by worms that burrow through human skin and enter the bloodstream. After growing in the lungs for a few weeks, they travel to veins that drain the intestines or bladder and remain there for up to 30 years, constantly laying eggs. Physicians estimate that the worms consume 350,000 red blood cells per hour.

Most of the damage, however, is done by the eggs produced by the female worms, which lay up to 3,000 per day. Some are carried in the blood to the liver and lungs, where they block these vital organs and eventually prove fatal. Others cause ulcers (open sores) in the bladder and intestines and pass out of the body with the feces. If any of these eggs reach fresh water, they hatch. The resulting larvae then infect various snails that live in canals, irrigation channels, and slow-moving rivers. The snail vectors spread the disease by releasing more parasite eggs into the water. The resulting larvae then look for a host, such as a person swimming in the water. They enter the human body through the skin, beginning the cycle again.

Recent research has revealed that the worms that cause schistosomiasis are attracted to a human hormone that is always present in veins and that drains into the intestine. The hormone tells the worms they are in the right place to lay their eggs. This fact may help scientists find a way to develop a vaccine against the worms.

Control of the disease depends on reducing the numbers of snails that spread it, preventing people from coming into contact with infected water, and preventing the water from becoming infected with human waste in the first place. Unfortunately, this is often difficult to do.

In Egypt, for example, where about 20 percent of the population suffer from schistosomiasis, the Nile River is the center of life for rural communities. Without the Nile River, many people would not be able to make a living, and the whole way of life would have to change. Simply killing the snail vectors that live in the Nile River would have an effect on the supply of fish.

Developing defenses

The human body's natural immune system—its ability to resist disease—can offer little defense against parasites. The body identifies its own tissues and those of parasites by detecting chemical markers on the surface of cells. Many internal parasites, such as tapeworms, steal the chemical markers used by the host's body. This makes them appear to be part of the body—invisible to the host's immune system. The malaria parasite protects itself by hiding inside human blood cells.

Since the immune system does not react to the presence of parasites, it is very difficult to develop vaccines against parasitic diseases. Another problem is the cost of developing new drugs, which can amount to billions of dollars. Often, the countries that are most badly affected by parasites, and where the research is most needed, are too poor even to buy existing drugs. In Europe and the United States, where there is enough money for the research and the necessary scientific and technical knowledge to carry it out, antiparasite drugs are not a priority. Drug companies focus their research on developing drugs for the illnesses suffered by people who can afford to pay for them.

A worldwide problem

Parasitic diseases are not only a problem of the developing countries. In developed countries, parasitic diseases are still a problem. For example, tapeworms are found on farms in North America and Europe, as well as in many other parts of the world. The worms infect farm animals, such as cattle and pigs. They live in these animals' intestines and absorb the food digested by their hosts. The worms produce cysts, which generally pass out with the feces. The cysts lie on the ground or vegetation until they are eaten by another animal. Sometimes the cysts embed themselves in the host's muscle and can be passed on to new hosts who eat the infected meat. Pig tapeworms, which are common in subtropical regions, can be passed to humans in this way. Someone with tapeworms might have several medical problems, and cysts that embed in their muscles might become dangerously large.

West Nile virus is carried by mosquitoes, which pass it to birds, horses, and humans. This virus causes a headache and fever, and in rare cases it can

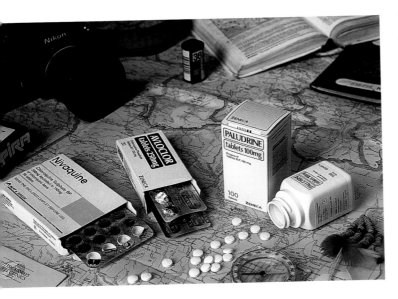

> ## DID YOU KNOW?
>
> Not all parasites are animals. Some familiar plants, such as mistletoe or the world's largest flower, *Rafflesia*, are parasites. Parasitic plants do not have roots like other plants. Instead, they steal water and nutrients through a structure called a haustorium, which has rootlike structures that grow inside the host plant's trunk. Mistletoe has leaves like other plants, and it harnesses the energy in sunlight to make its food by photosynthesis in the normal way. However, other plant parasites, such as dodder, cannot do this. They get all their food from the host plant.
>
> All fungi are parasites or saprophytes (organisms that feed on dead tissue). Most fungi consist of a mass of thin threads, called hyphae, that absorb food and water. The hyphae of parasitic fungi penetrate the host plant's tissues and absorb the water, nutrients, and food stored by the plant.

cause a deadly inflammation of the brain. In 1999, West Nile virus was reported in the United States for the first time. It is thought that the parasite was brought into the area from Africa by mosquitoes traveling on international passenger aircraft.

Helpful parasites

Some parasites are used to fight pests. Each parasite is selected as a natural enemy of a specific pest. For example, parasitic nematodes are used to combat weevils. Nematodes are tiny worms that carry bacteria in their gut. When a worm bites a host weevil, the bacteria enter the host and kill it.

◀ *Antimalarial drugs do not prevent infection. Instead, they wipe out malarial parasites before they can damage the body. These drugs can be taken safely for only a few months at a time.*

See *also:* CELL • DISEASE • VACCINATION

Particle accelerator

Particle accelerators are machines that are used to fire particles smaller than atoms at extremely high speeds. These fast-moving particles may be used to split atoms or made to collide with each other. In both cases, new particles are produced.

Nuclear scientists use huge particle accelerators to investigate the structure of the atomic nucleus and the particles from which it is made. The first experiments with accelerators were designed to investigate the center, or nucleus, of the atom. As the nucleus was split in the process, the machines became known as "atom-smashers." However, "nucleus-smashers" might have been a better name. Smashing an atom is relatively simple to do and does not need an accelerator.

The outer parts of atoms consist of particles called electrons, and these are easy to remove. Just giving a body a positive electrical charge will remove some of the electrons from its atoms. However, the nuclei of most atoms consist of particles called protons and neutrons bound tightly together. The nucleus must therefore be bombarded by fast-moving particles if it is to be changed in any way.

The nature of a chemical element is determined by the number of particles in the nuclei of its atoms, so bombarding a nucleus can cause a new element to be formed. For centuries, scientists called alchemists have tried to turn inexpensive metals, such as lead, into precious metals, such as gold. This process is now possible using a particle accelerator, although gold produced in this way would be extremely expensive.

Modern particle accelerators are very powerful machines. The largest ones rarely fire atoms. Instead, they use subatomic particles, such as electrons and protons. The energy contained within these particles is then used to create more unusual particles when they hit a target. This was predicted by German-born U.S. physicist Albert Einstein (1879–1955), who said that energy and mass are interchangeable.

▶ This aerial view shows the European Organization for Nuclear Research (CERN) particle accelerator near Geneva, Switzerland. CERN has two storage rings. The larger one (shown by a white ring) is inside a tunnel that is 17 miles (27 kilometers) long. The smaller boost ring runs for around 4 miles (7 kilometers) inside the larger one. The rings actually cross the border (shown) between France and Switzerland.

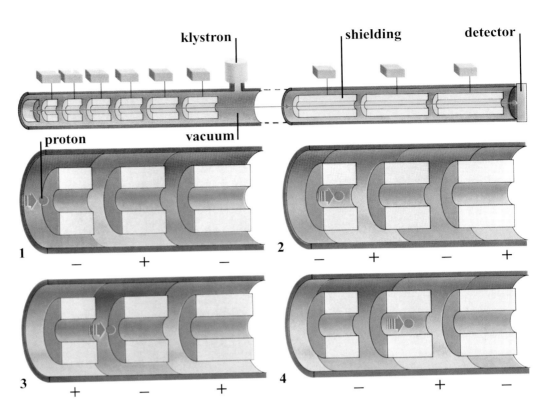

▶ *A variable electrical field set up by a klystron accelerates protons inside a linear accelerator. (1) A proton enters the tube and accelerates toward a negatively charged drift tube. (2) While the proton is shielded inside the first tube, the charge on the tube is reduced, and a negative charge is placed on the next tube. (3) The proton emerges from the first tube and accelerates toward the second tube. (4) The proton is shielded again as the charge on the tube is reduced, and a charge is placed on the next tube. The process repeats, and the proton speeds toward its target.*

Linear accelerators

A linear accelerator moves particles in straight lines. It is the simplest type of accelerator. Some are as long as 2 miles (3 kilometers). One type of linear accelerator consists of a cylinder containing a series of metal shielding tubes arranged in a straight line. Protons, electrons, or other particles are injected into one end of the cylinder. These subatomic particles are electrically charged, so other electrical charges will attract or repel them. Opposite charges attract each other; like charges repel.

For example, a proton with its positive charge will be attracted by negative charges and repelled by positive charges. In the accelerator, a device called a klystron produces a rapidly changing electrical field that passes along the walls of the cylinder. Each part of the cylinder is given a negative charge and then a positive charge in a repeating pattern.

The system is arranged so that a particle entering the cylinder is first attracted by an opposite electrical charge on the walls in front of it. This makes it accelerate (speed up). Farther up the tube, the charge of the field changes, which would push against the motion of the particle. By this time, however, the particle is shielded from the field by the first tube, so the particle continues on without being slowed. When it emerges from the tube, an oppositely charged field is again in front of it, so it is accelerated once more. Along the length of the cylinder, the particle is accelerated each time it is exposed. The more it accelerates, the farther it travels while the field changes. So the shielding tubes are made longer and longer. This arrangement ensures that the particle remains shielded until the field in that part of the tube has the correct charge.

In practice, a stream of particles is fired along the cylinder. Magnets are used to focus the particles in a narrow beam. This beam smashes into a detector at the far end of the cylinder.

Circular accelerators

In circular accelerators, the particles pass the same accelerating devices many times. So it is easier to accelerate the particles to high speeds. (To achieve the same speeds in a linear accelerator would require a tube many miles long.) The simplest circular accelerators are cyclotrons. These have a beam of particles that is fed into a gap between two

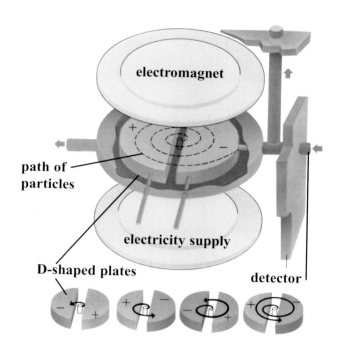

In a cyclotron, particles are released between the D-shaped plates. A fixed magnetic field from the electromagnet and a changing electrical field between the plates both influence the particles. As a result, they accelerate in a widening spiral path.

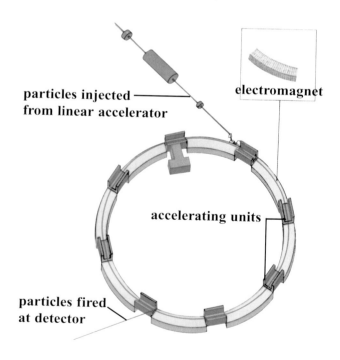

The synchrotron accelerates particles injected into a vacuum tube. Powerful electromagnets guide the particles into a circular path. They accelerate inside to reach high speeds before colliding with a detector.

D-shaped plates. An alternating electrical field and a fixed magnetic field make the particle beam move in a spiral path.

Synchro-cyclotrons are more powerful types of accelerators. Inside these devices, the electrical field is made to change in step with the particles moving across the plates. This process produces a faster final speed than basic cyclotrons.

Synchrotrons

The most powerful types of accelerators are synchrotrons. These use electromagnets and radio waves to accelerate beams of particles around large circular tubes, called storage rings. The beam is accelerated around the ring until it reaches the required speed. Then the beam is fired at a target, or directed into another beam of particles.

Inside a synchrotron, the beam of particles is first sped up in a linear accelerator. There, the beam is also divided into pulses. The beam is then passed to a boost ring. This ring is lined with electromagnets. These are magnets that can be turned on and off using an electrical current. The magnets are used to make a changing magnetic field, which increases the energy in the beam of particles.

The beam is then passed to the main storage ring. This may be several miles long. At points around the storage ring, magnets are positioned to keep the beam traveling in the correct path around the ring. It is important for scientists to control the exact location of the beam because it is only a few billionths of an inch wide.

Storage rings are used to build up large amounts of high-energy particles. Many pulses produced by the accelerator are concentrated into a fine stream. This stream may contain more than 100 times more particles than could be produced by an accelerator on it own.

Synchrotrons are designed for accelerating a particular type of particle. For example, the Large Hadron Collider at the European Organization for Nuclear Research (CERN) in Switzerland is used to accelerate subatomic particles such as protons. Other synchrotrons are built to carry smaller particles such as electrons and positrons.

▶ *The SLAC particle accelerator in California has two tubes. The upper tube carries low-energy particles, and the lower ring carries out high-energy experiments.*

The most powerful proton synchrotron is at the Fermi National Accelerator Laboratory (Fermilab) near Chicago. The highest-energy electron synchrotron is at CERN.

Uses of synchrotrons

Beams in the storage ring may be directed onto a target. A detector is then used to observe the results of the collision. Scientists also observe collisions between beams of particles. The boost ring can feed beams of particles into the storage ring in both directions. When they are at the correct speed and energy level, the beams are made to collide.

When a high-energy beam hits a target or other particles, huge amounts of energy are released. This energy forms into rare and unusual particles. These particles only exist for a tiny fraction of a second, but they can be detected by scientists in that time.

Bubble chambers are most commonly used to detect collisions. These are filled with a liquid. When the high-energy particles produced by the

collisions pass through the chamber, they leave a trail of bubbles. Scientists can determine which particles are produced by the direction, speed, and size of the trails.

High-speed collisions generally take place inside the storage ring or at an experimental station nearby. However, at CERN a concentrated beam of neutrinos is being fired from one of the accelerators out into the air. The beam is targeted at a detector 450 miles (730 kilometers) away, near Rome, Italy. Neutrinos are tiny and almost massless particles. They are totally harmless, so a beam leaving the accelerator is not dangerous. In fact, millions of neutrinos are passing through a person's body all the time without having any effect. They are so harmless because neutrinos very rarely interact with other particles. This quality makes it almost impossible to get them to collide with a detector— they just go straight through it.

▲ *At CERN, two storage rings intersect. The rings carry beams of high-speed protons.*

See also: ATOM AND MOLECULE • ELECTRICITY • ELECTROMAGNETISM • PARTICLE DETECTOR • PARTICLE PHYSICS • PHYSICS • X-RAY

Particle detector

Particle detectors are used to find the tiniest parts, or particles, of matter that make up the universe. Particles cannot be seen even with the most powerful microscopes, but detectors can show how they move and what effect they have on each other.

▲ *A giant bubble chamber, being built at the CERN accelerator in Switzerland, contains 1,200 cubic feet (35 cubic meters) of liquid hydrogen. The liquid is compressed by pistons weighing 2⅕ tons (2 tonnes).*

Around two hundred different types of particles, such as mesons and photons, have been discovered so far by various kinds of particle detectors. Due to the small size of these particles, it is only by looking at traces of where they have traveled, and what they have done to other particles, that anything can be learned about them.

To trace the path of a charged particle, most detectors use a device known as an ionization chamber, which is usually filled with a solid, liquid, or gas. When a fast-moving, electrically charged particle passes through the chamber, it collides with some of the atoms there and knocks electrons off them. An atom that has lost or gained electrons becomes charged itself and is known as an ion. Scientists can detect the ionization and learn something about the particles that caused it.

Nuclear emulsions

Photographic plates coated with chemicals called nuclear emulsions were the first detectors. Similar to other photographic films, these emulsions turn black when exposed to radiation, such as light. When a particle hits the plate, it leaves a dark track.

Nuclear emulsions were used to detect the particles in cosmic rays. Cosmic rays are streams of high-energy particles that come from outer space. However, the tracks in the emulsion do not tell scientists when the particles passed by. Nor do they show which particles produced them. The tracks could be made by the particles in the cosmic rays or the electrons released during ionization.

Accurate detectors

More accurate detectors are used to study subatomic particles. These tiny particles make up atoms. All of them are far too small to see, and many exist only for a fraction of a second. Scientists produce the subatomic particles inside large machines called particle accelerators. These accelerate streams of basic particles, such as protons or electrons, to huge speeds. Then the streams are smashed into targets or into another stream of particles. As a result of these collisions, large amounts of energy are released, and this energy turns into a range of unusual particles.

In this way, hundreds of new particles have been discovered. Complex detectors are needed to observe such tiny and short-lived objects. The detectors used to do this include bubble and cloud chambers and spark detectors.

Leaving traces

Bubble chambers are containers filled with liquid. When a particle passes through the chamber, it leaves a trail of bubbles that can be photographed. Cloud chambers are similar but less sensitive. They are glass-domed containers filled with vapor. When particles pass through a cloud chamber, they leave a trail of liquid droplets that can be photographed.

Bubble chambers not only detect particles, they also allow scientists to see how they interact with each other. The trails are photographed through a window in the top of the chamber to give a permanent record of what takes place inside. By studying the movements and interactions of the particles, scientists can learn about the physical characteristics of each type of particle.

How a bubble chamber works

Bubble chambers were invented by U.S physicist Donald A. Glaser (1926–) in 1952. He thought of a method for using the way a liquid forms bubbles to detect the presence of particles. Bubbles form when a liquid boils (turns into a gas). Liquids boil when they are heated, but the temperature at which they boil depends on the pressure acting on them. If the liquid is under high pressure, it will not boil until it gets much hotter than usual. If it is under low pressure, the liquid will boil at a lower temperature.

For example, water boils at 212°F (100°C) in normal conditions. At the top of the very highest mountains, however, water boils at about ten degrees less because the pressure of the air pushing down on the liquid water is less at the top of the mountain than at the bottom.

When a liquid starts to boil, the bubbles begin to form around the charged particles, such as ions, in the liquid. When high-energy particles pass through the liquid, they make ions. For bubble chambers to detect these particles, the liquid inside must be made to boil at the precise moment that the particles are passing through the chamber.

▶ *Photographs can reveal the trails caused by particles in a bubble chamber. These trails were produced by neutrinos colliding with electrons.*

The bubble chamber is filled with a superheated liquid. A superheated liquid is one that has been heated up to well above its natural boiling point. However, it has been kept as a liquid by exerting huge pressures on it to stop it from boiling.

The liquid used most often is liquid hydrogen. Hydrogen is usually a gas and has one of the lowest boiling points of any substance. It becomes a liquid at −421°F (−252°C). The liquid is squeezed by a piston to high pressures and is therefore at a temperature slightly above its boiling point—it is superheated. Despite being superheated, the liquid hydrogen is still extremely cold.

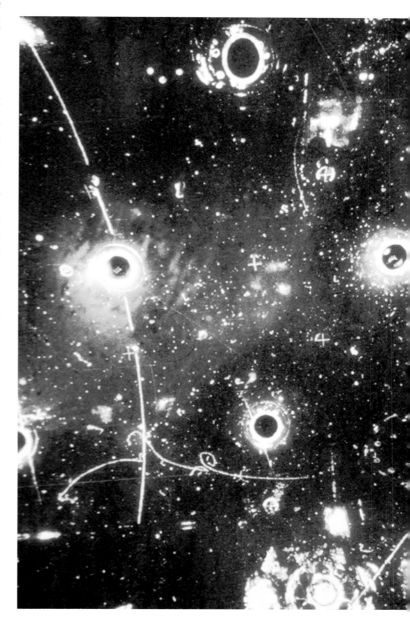

When the beam of particles is fired into the liquid, the piston in the chamber is lowered, which reduces the pressure and causes the liquid to boil quickly. This action is similar to the way a bottle of soda fizzes when the lid is loosened. The drink is under high pressure in the bottle. Opening the lid reduces the pressure, and bubbles form.

Inside the chamber, the first tiny bubbles form around the ions that are produced as the particles move through the liquid. These are photographed through windows in the top of the chamber. The images produced are then fed into a computer to make it easier to study them. All this takes place in just a few thousandths of a second, so it must be controlled very carefully.

The chamber of liquid is surrounded by powerful magnets. These produce a magnetic field that runs through the liquid. This force field bends the paths of different particles in different ways, and this helps scientists identify them.

All the equipment is also surrounded by a thick iron cylinder. This cylinder shields any sensitive equipment from the effects of the magnets inside. It also stops harmful radiation produced by the high-energy particles from leaking out.

Spark chambers

These particle detectors have two arrangements of thin wires with a small gap between them. The chamber is filled with a gas. As a particle approaches the spark chamber, a large current is passed along all the wires. As the particle passes through the gap, it smashes the atoms of gas,

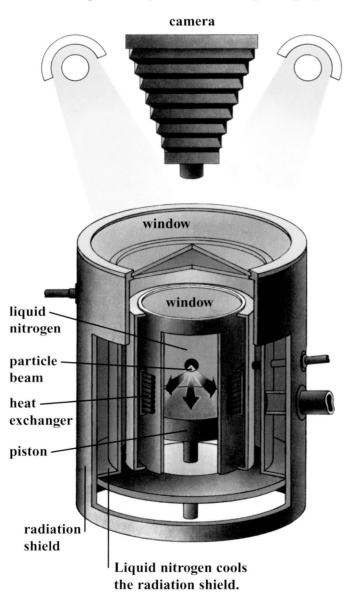

▲ *Inside a liquid hydrogen bubble chamber, the heat exchange system cools the liquid hydrogen in the cooling tank. The radiation shield stops any dangerous particles from getting out of the tank.*

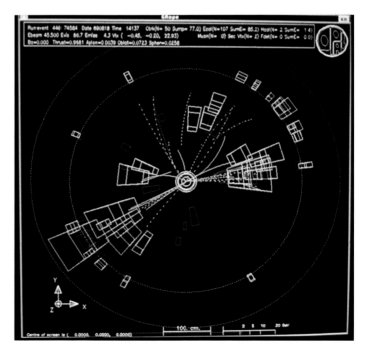

▲ *Bubble-chamber pictures are converted into computer images, which help to present the data in a way that can be analyzed more easily. This image shows a Z particle breaking apart.*

▲ *This detector at CERN is used to observe protons and antiprotons colliding inside a large ring. When these particles collide, they annihilate each other and release a large amount of energy.*

ionizing them. Ionized gas conducts electricity, and a short burst of current travels through the gas across the gap from one wire to the other. This creates a spark as the gas around the current gets very hot. Spark chambers are combined, so a particle's path is marked by a trail of sparks.

The gap between the wires makes it is hard to mark the exact position of the particle. To overcome this, sheets of aluminum are sometimes used instead of wires. In this case, the particle produces a continuous glowing streak, which is captured by a video camera.

Particle counters

It is often important to count particles, especially when they are dangerous, such as the particles produced by radioactivity. The simplest counter is the Geiger-Müller detector, which is a tube of gas with a wire running along its center. The wire is charged by electricity. Particles come into the tube through a window at one end. They then ionize the gas atoms in the counter. The electrons released from the ions cling to the wire and produce a tiny pulse of electricity. Every pulse is counted, and it also produces a click in a loudspeaker. High numbers of particles make so many clicks that the speaker produces a high-pitched buzzing noise.

Almost undetectable

Neutrinos are smaller than electrons and have no charge. They are very hard to detect because they do not cause ionizations and most pass through detectors without having any effect at all. Neutrinos from space are detected as they pass through Earth by huge detectors deep underground. In 1987, neutrinos produced by an exploding star hit Earth. There were 65 billion neutrinos for every square inch (10 billion per square centimeter) of the Earth's surface. However, only 19 of these neutrinos were actually observed.

See also: ATOM AND MOLECULE • MAGNETISM • PARTICLE ACCELERATOR • PARTICLE PHYSICS

Particle physics

The universe consists of tiny particles, such as electrons and protons. Particles physics is the study of these objects. New particles are still being discovered. Physicists are studying the relationships among these particles and the forces they exert on each other.

Scientists working in the field of particle physicists are investigating how everything in the universe is put together. To scientists, a model of the way something works does not have to be actually made from materials. It is simply a description of the way it works and how everything fits together. So according to one scientific model of the universe, everything is made from a range of basic particles. These particles are held together by fundamental (basic) forces. The four forces in the universe are gravity, the weak nuclear force, the electromagnetic force, and the strong nuclear force.

Building the model

Around 2,500 years ago, Greek philosopher Democritus (c. 460–c. 370 BCE) suggested that the universe is made up of atoms . He said that matter could not be divided up forever. Eventually it would become impossible to split a substance into smaller pieces. He named each of these smallest units an "atomos." The word atom comes from the Greek word *atomos*, which means "indivisible."

In the eighteenth century, Democritus's ideas were used by the first chemists to help them understand how different elements were formed. Therefore, until a century ago, most scientists accepted the theory that matter was made up of combinations of different kinds of atoms. Atoms were still considered the smallest particles of matter that could exist. Then, in 1897, English physicist J. J. Thomson (1856–1940) discovered electrons, tiny particles that were subatomic—smaller than atoms.

▲ *Subatomic particles are detected in a bubble chamber. This chamber contains a liquid. When particles travel through at high speed, they make a trail of tiny bubbles, which can be photographed.*

In 1911, New Zealand–born British physicist Ernest Rutherford (1871–1937) proposed that the atom is a miniature "solar system" with electrons circling around a central nucleus like the planets orbit the Sun. The electrons have a negative electrical charge, and the nucleus has a positive charge.

Later experiments showed that the positive charges in the nucleus are carried by subatomic particles identical to the nuclei of hydrogen atoms. They became known as protons. In 1932, a third fundamental particle was discovered, which was similar in mass to the proton. However, this particle was neutral; it had no electric charge. Therefore, it was called the neutron.

The proton and neutron were the main particles in the nucleus. However, objects with the same charge push away from each other, and scientists did not know why protons in the nucleus did not fly apart. It was suggested that smaller particles—named mesons—kept the protons in place.

Over the next few decades, many other fundamental particles, including the meson, were discovered. Physicists found many of these in cosmic rays—the shower of particles that hits Earth's atmosphere from outer space. For example, the first mesons were found in cosmic rays by a detector on top of a mountain. New particles were also made by firing atoms and subatomic particles at each other inside particle accelerators. These machines were nicknamed "atom-smashers."

Particle accelerators use powerful magnets and electric fields to make charged particles speed up to huge speeds. In the largest accelerators, the particles are fired along tunnels several miles long or around large underground loops. Eventually the particles are aimed at detectors or made to collide with each other. The particles impact at such huge speeds that they break up and form different types of particles. As the power of particle accelerators has increased, many more new particles have been discovered.

Particle characteristics

More than two hundred different fundamental particles have been discovered so far. They are identified by their basic physical characteristics, including mass, electric charge, and how they spin. Different particles have a range of life spans. The proton and electron are entirely stable. However, most other subatomic particles exist only for a few nanoseconds (thousand-millionths of a second) or even picoseconds (million-millionths).

As well as "normal" particles, such as electrons and protons, there are antiparticles. These particles are the same as normal ones in every way except one, such as electric charge. The antiparticle of the electron, for example, appears frequently in radioactive decay. It has the same mass as the ordinary electron, but it has a positive electric charge. It is usually called a positron. There are antiparticles to the other normal particles, too. Even particles without an electric charge, such as

▶ *The Stanford Linear Accelerator (SLAC) is a 2-mile (3.2-kilometer) particle accelerator in California. Electrons and positrons smash into each other inside the accelerator to make unusual subatomic particles.*

neutrons, have antiparticles. Like a neutron, an antineutron is neutral, and therefore the two particles have identical physical characteristics, but the two have just one difference. When a particle and antiparticle hit each other, they are both completely destroyed and release lots of energy. Therefore, when a neutron hits an antineutron, the same happens. When a neutron hits another neutron, they just bounce off each other.

Families of particles

There is no good method of classifying subatomic particles, but the following is a common way of doing so. The simplest and smallest particles are perhaps the most baffling. They include the photon and the neutrino. Photons have no rest mass but carry energy at the speed of light (186,000 miles or 300,000 kilometer per second). Most physicists now believe that neutrinos have a tiny rest mass but can carry a great deal of energy. Both photons and neutrinos have the property of spin (the rotation on an axis, which produces angular momentum).

Photons are the tiny "packets" of energy present in light and other radiation, such as radio waves, heat, and X-rays. Photons belong to a group of particles called bosons. Bosons are particles that carry, or mediate, forces between other particles.

Neutrinos are released during nuclear fission. They are almost impossible to detect because they can pass through most matter without affecting it

at all. They belong to another group of particles called leptons. Leptons are very small and light particles that do not interact with other particles very much. The most familiar lepton is the electron, but they also include muons and positrons.

The largest group of fundamental particles are much heavier. They are called hadrons. These particles also interact with each other more strongly than the leptons. Hadrons are themselves divided up in several ways. The smaller hadrons form a subgroup called mesons. These are short-lived particles; some have an electrical charge, and others are neutral. The mesons include the pions and kaons. There are three kinds of pions, for example, which differ in their electric charge. One is positively charged, one is neutral, and the other, the antipion, is negatively charged.

The next group of hadrons contain heavier particles called nucleons. As the name suggests, these particles are the ones found in atomic nuclei, such as protons and neutrons. The nucleons have a

mass about 1,840 times heavier than an electron and about four times more than the mesons. Some rare types of hadrons are heavier still. These are called hyperons. (Often scientists group the hadrons and hyperons together as baryons.) Hyperons include short-lived particles, such as the lambda, sigma, xi, and omega particles.

By far the heaviest particles that have been discovered so far are the W and Z particles. These are force-carrying particles involved in the weak nuclear force. They were discovered in the 1980s and are about 90 times heavier than protons.

Most of these fundamental particles were identified in particle accelerators in the 1950s and 1960s. By the 1970s, scientists realized that the particles they had found did not explain the behavior of all the hadrons. Something was missing. It was suggested that hadrons were not fundamental particles themselves. Instead, they were made up of even smaller particles called quarks (and antiquarks). Mesons contain two quarks,

SOME SUBATOMIC PARTICLES

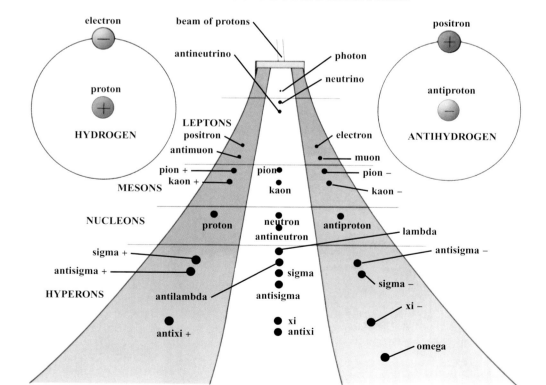

◄ Some of the best-known fundamental atomic particles are shown in this imaginary beam produced by bombarding a target with protons. They are shown in order of increasing mass. In the center are shown the particles that are neutral. Those on the left are positively charged, while those on the right are negatively charged. At the top left is a simplified diagram of the normal hydrogen atom. At the top right is a diagram of what an antihydrogen atom would be like. It has a positron circling around an antiproton nucleus.

× 69576

▲ *The results of a collision between protons and antiprotons at a Swiss particle accelerator in 1982 (shown as a computer-generated image above) proved the existence of the W particle.*

while nucleons are made up of three. (The hyperons are combinations of several more quarks.) Scientists have identified six types, or flavors, of quarks: "up," "down," "top," "bottom," "charm," and "strange." The top quark was the last flavor to be observed in a particle accelerator. It was discovered in 1994.

Fundamental forces

Just as there are fundamental particles, so there are fundamental forces, or interactions, that govern the way the particles behave. However, these forces are carried by particles themselves. Force-carrier particles are called bosons. Particles exchange the bosons, and a force is observed to be acting on the particles. Photons are the most familiar boson.

The force of gravity acts between any bodies that have mass. It is this force that prevents people and all things on Earth from flying off into space. Unlike most of the other forces, gravity acts across huge distances, such as between the planets and the Sun. The graviton is the boson that carries the force of gravity. Similar to the photon, scientists believe that the graviton has no rest mass and thus far have been unable to detect them.

The strong nuclear force is what binds the particles in the nucleus. It acts between all hadrons and is effective over very short distances—about the diameter of the nucleus. The strong force is carried by tiny, almost massless particles called gluons. The gluons are exchanged by the quarks that make up the atom's protons and neutrons.

The electromagnetic force exists between any particles carrying a charge. It is the force that keeps the negatively charged electrons in orbit around the positive nucleus. The force also makes magnets attract some metals. Photons carry this force.

The electromagnetic force is about one hundred times weaker than the strong force. However, it is several million times stronger than the other force that acts between particles—the weak force. The weak force is involved in the breakup of nucleon particles, such as in radioactivity. It acts on all particles, but its effect is overcome by the other forces, except in the case of the leptons. The weak nuclear force is carried by W and Z particles.

The latest idea in particle physics is that particles behave like strings. These strings vibrate in several dimensions, and each vibration defines how the strings, or particles, interact with each other.

See also: ATOM AND MOLECULE • ELECTRICITY • PARTICLE ACCELERATOR • PARTICLE DETECTOR

Pasteur, Louis

French chemist Louis Pasteur is the founding father of the science of microbiology. Pasteur suggested that bacteria cause disease and showed how yeast causes fermentation. A process called pasteurization, which uses heat to kill germs in drinks such as milk, is named for him.

Louis Pasteur was born in 1822 at Dole, France. His father was a poor tanner who prepared skins for the leather industry. As a child, Pasteur was not very academic, and his main interest was painting. However, an inspiring teacher set Pasteur on the road toward science, and by his early twenties he was famous for his inventive experiments.

In 1854, Pasteur began a series of experiments in Lille, France, to help vinegar and winemakers, who were losing a lot of money because their produce was going sour. For example, vinegar often spoiled as it was being made from beet juice. In 1857, Pasteur realized that tiny organisms called yeasts—the same microorganisms that fermented fruit and turned into alcohol—were gradually spoiling the vinegar and wine. Until then, people had thought that fermentation was a chemical process. By discovering that microorganisms were responsible, Pasteur brought about huge improvements in the manufacture of fermentation products such as beer, vinegar, and wine.

Even more importantly, Pasteur showed that microorganisms develop from other micro-organisms and do not just appear spontaneously as scientists had once thought.

Landmark discoveries

Two other great discoveries emerged from Pasteur's study of fermentation. First, Pasteur found that he could stop some kinds of bacteria from growing by exposing them to oxygen in the air. He also found

▲ Louis Pasteur found that microorganisms play a crucial role in many natural processes, such as fermentation, and in the development of many diseases.

that other bacteria needed air to grow. He called those bacteria that were killed by oxygen "anaerobic" bacteria, and those that needed air "aerobic" bacteria.

Pasteur's next great discovery came from his studies of winemaking. He found that heating wine to a certain temperature would kill off yeast and stop it from multiplying. This heating process is

* Column numbering system recommended by the International Union of Pure and Applied Chemistry (IUPAC)
** Column numbering system recommended by the Chemical Abstracts Service

1* Ia**	2 IIa	3 IIIb	4 IVb	5 Vb	6 VIb	7 VIIb	8	9 VIIIb	10	11 Ib	12 IIb	13 IIIa	14 IVa	15 Va	16 VIa	17 VIIa	18 O
1 H	2 IIa																2 He
3 Li	4 Be											5 B	6 C	7 N	8 O	9 F	10 Ne
11 Na	12 Mg											13 Al	14 Si	15 P	16 S	17 Cl	18 Ar
19 K	20 Ca	21 Sc	22 Ti	23 V	24 Cr	25 Mn	26 Fe	27 Co	28 Ni	29 Cu	30 Zn	31 Ga	32 Ge	33 As	34 Se	35 Br	36 Kr
37 Rb	38 Sr	39 Y	40 Zr	41 Nb	42 Mo	43 Tc	44 Ru	45 Rh	46 Pd	47 Ag	48 Cd	49 In	50 Sn	51 Sb	52 Te	53 I	54 Xe
55 Cs	56 Ba	57* La	72 Hf	73 Ta	74 W	75 Re	76 Os	77 Ir	78 Pt	79 Au	80 Hg	81 Tl	82 Pb	83 Bi	84 Po	85 At	86 Rn
87 Fr	88 Ra	89+ Ac	104 Rf	105 Db	106 Sg	107 Bh	108 Hs	109 Mt	110 Ds	111 Rg	112 Uub						

group / period

*58 Ce	59 Pr	60 Nd	61 Pm	62 Sm	63 Eu	64 Gd	65 Tb	66 Dy	67 Ho	68 Er	69 Tm	70 Yb	71 Lu
+90 Th	91 Pa	92 U	93 Np	94 Pu	95 Am	96 Cm	97 Bk	98 Cf	99 Es	100 Fm	101 Md	102 No	103 Lr

- hydrogen
- alkali metals
- alkaline earth metals
- lanthanides
- actinides
- transition metals
- other metals
- metaloids
- other nonmetals
- halogens
- inert gases

▲ This is the modern periodic table of the elements. The columns show the groups of elements, and the rows show the periods. Each period begins with a very reactive metal and ends with an inert (nonreactive) gas. The elements between also follow a periodic pattern.

triads." He found groups of three elements in which the chemical properties of the lightest and heaviest could be used to predict the properties of the element in between. Lithium, sodium, and potassium are an example of one of Döbereiner's triads (look at where these elements lie on the periodic table to see why this works).

A major step toward the classification of the elements was the discovery of relative atomic weights. This stemmed from work by Italian scientist Amedeo Avogadro (1776–1856). Avogadro showed that at a constant temperature and pressure, certain gases react in predictable ratios.

For example, one gallon (3.75 liters) of nitrogen reacts with three gallons (11.25 liters) of hydrogen to produce two gallons (7.5 liters) of ammonia.

Avogadro suggested that a certain volume of any gas contained a specific number of molecules. By weighing samples of different volumes of gases, he could calculate the masses of their atoms relative to each other. A gallon of oxygen weighed 16 times more than a gallon of hydrogen, so an atom of oxygen must be 16 times heavier than a hydrogen atom. Relative atomic weights were calculated for all the known elements based on carbon, which was given the value of 12. Italian chemist Stanislao Cannizzaro (1826–1910) showed that Avogadro's ideas could be used to deduce atomic weights and to figure out the formulas of compounds.

In 1862, French scientist Alexandre-Émile Béguyer de Chancourtois (1820–1896) was the first to relate the new findings of atomic weights to chemical periodicity. He drew the elements on a spiral divided into 16 parts, which ran around a cylinder. He noticed that some of Döbereiner's triads appeared together on his spiral, as did a tetrad (four elements with similar properties)—oxygen, sulfur, selenium, and tellurium. For this reason, he called his device a "telluric spiral."

Other parts of the spiral did not work as well. Boron and aluminum were linked, but they were followed by nickel, arsenic, lanthanum, and palladium—very different elements. Béguyer de Chancourtois had discovered the basics of periodicity, but he had gotten the frequency wrong.

Newlands's octave
Another chemist who nearly solved the puzzle of periodicity was English chemist John Newlands (1837–1898). In 1864, he made a table of elements increasing in atomic weight that covered seven columns. Noticing some periodicity, Newlands called his discovery the "law of octaves." He made some suggestions about missing elements but did not leave spaces for them on his final table. Newlands had trouble finding a publisher, and his research was dismissed by other scientists.

Chemists continued to wrestle with the concept of periodicity and atomic weight data with mixed success. Publications were met with derision and hostility. Then, in 1869, Russian chemist Dmitry Mendeleyev (1834–1907) entered the scene.

Learning from valency
Mendeleyev also arranged the elements by atomic weight, but what sets his research apart from his contemporaries is that he discovered a repeating pattern unnoticed by other chemists. This pattern was the valency of the elements. Valency is a measure of the combining power of an element. Lithium, the second element in Mendeleyev's list, had a valency of 1. This was followed by beryllium (2), boron (3), carbon (4), nitrogen (3), oxygen (2), and fluorine (1). The pattern of rising and falling valency was repeated for the next set of elements.

> ## DID YOU KNOW?
>
> Uranium has 92 protons in the nucleus of each atom. Elements with higher atomic numbers are called transuranic elements. With the exception of neptunium and plutonium, all the transuranic elements are made artificially. Some may form in space in supernovas, but they are all radioactive and generally extremely unstable, decaying to more stable elements very quickly.
>
> Scientists make transuranic elements in particle accelerators. Tiny particles are smashed into heavy atoms to produce new elements. The discovery of this technique led to many discoveries in the mid-twentieth century. For example, element 101 was named Mendelevium (Md) in honor of Mendeleyev. To date, scientists have made elements with atoms containing up to 112 protons. Heavier elements are possible—the discovery of elements 116 and 118 was announced in 2003 by U.S. scientists but later retracted; however, attempts to make elements with such massive atoms continue.

▲ Bromine (Br), as contained in this jar, is highly toxic. Bromine is the only nonmetallic element that is a liquid at room temperature, but it is weakly bonded and readily vaporizes at room temperature.

▶ *These brilliant blue crystals are hydrated copper sulfate. Copper (or cupric) sulfate ($CuSO_4$) is the most widely used copper compound. Copper is a transition metal, one of the most useful of the metals. Transition metals are characterized by their strength and ductility (ability to be stretched), their high melting and boiling points, and their ability to easily form compounds.*

Mendeleyev's table followed this valency trend. The columns produced gave elements with similar chemical properties. The first column, for example, included lithium, sodium, and potassium. All had a valency of 1. Mendeleyev's columns are now called groups. The group 1 elements are referred to as the alkali metals.

Dealing with anomalies

Mendeleyev was prepared to place elements in his table in what appeared to be the wrong groups. For example, most chemists thought that the chemical formula for beryllium oxide was Be_2O_3. This would give beryllium a valency of 3. However, some chemists thought that the true formula for the oxide was BeO, giving beryllium a valency of 2. Mendeleyev had a gap in his table in group 2, so he placed beryllium there—correctly.

Mendeleyev was also prepared to place elements out of order in terms of atomic weight. With an atomic weight of 128, tellurium should have come after iodine (atomic weight 127). However, its chemical properties suggested that tellurium should appear in the group before iodine. Mendeleyev assumed there had been mistakes in

DID YOU KNOW?

Mendeleyev explained away some of the problems with his periodic table as errors in the determination of atomic weights. However, Mendeleyev was wrong. The position of an element in the table is determined by the number of protons in the nuclei of its atoms, which was a discovery made after Mendeleyev's death. This figure is called the atomic number. The anomalies Mendeleyev and other chemists had to cope with were due to the existence of isotopes. Take a carbon atom. It has six protons in its nucleus, so its atomic number is six. This cannot change; add an extra proton and the carbon atom becomes a nitrogen atom. Most carbon atoms have six neutrons, but some have eight neutrons. These atoms are still carbon, with all the same chemical properties, but they have a higher atomic weight. In this example, the isotope is called carbon-14.

the calculations of weight. Chemists now know that the measurements were correct, but the atomic weights were muddied by the influence of isotopes—of which Mendeleyev had no knowledge. Iodine has a single isotope of mass 127. There are eight tellurium isotopes; the most abundant is tellurium-130. This raises the average atomic weight to 128, a fact that confused Mendeleyev.

Criticized but vindicated

Perhaps the greatest vindication of Mendeleyev's table was provided by what he left out rather than what was included. There were a number of gaps in the table. Critics leapt on omissions as a sign that Mendeleyev was wrong. However, Mendeleyev fought back by suggesting that some elements had not yet been discovered. He even predicted the chemical properties of these unknown elements, one of which he named eka-aluminum.

▼ *This picture shows iodine (I). Iodine does not exist naturally as an ore. Most iodine used is extracted from seaweeds. Iodine is a halogen element. The name halogen derives from the Greek words* hal *(salt) and* gen *(to produce), because all halogens produce sodium salts of similar properties.*

In 1875, French chemist Paul-Emile Lecoq de Boisbaudran (1838–1912) discovered a new element, whose properties matched those that Mendeleyev had predicted for eka-aluminum. The new element, called gallium, proved that Mendeleyev's table was correct.

How does periodicity work?

Mendeleyev arrived at the right answer but for the wrong reasons. Chemists now know that periodicity is related to the number of protons in the nucleus—this is the atomic number. In turn, it is linked to the number of electrons orbiting the nucleus. Mendeleyev came to similar conclusions indirectly, through the related properties of atomic weight and valency. So, how do modern chemists explain periodicity with the benefit of the century of research denied to Mendeleyev?

Electrons do not circle the nucleus at random distances. Instead, they travel in distinct orbits. These orbits group to form electron shells, each shell reflecting the energy level of the electrons it contains. Most atoms have a number of different electron shells.

Each electron shell can hold only a certain number of electrons. An inner shell holds two electrons; second shells and third shells hold eight and eighteen electrons, respectively. The maximum number of electrons found in each shell can be calculated by the formula:

$$2n^2$$

where "n" is the number of shells.

An element's chemical properties depend on the number of electrons in the outermost shell. Elements with a full outer shell do not react readily, if at all. Other elements react with each other by giving or receiving electrons to form complete outer shells.

Shells and orbitals

Although electrons cannot be seen directly, their motion can be described mathematically. Within each electron shell there are different patterns of

◄ *This picture shows a glowing nuclear fuel rod being placed in a cooling pond after it has been used. Nuclear fuel rods are produced from uranium (U), a member of the radioactive group of elements called actinides.*

motion possible. The allowable patterns of motion are called orbitals. The first shell has only one orbital, called an s orbital, which can hold one or two electrons. The second shell includes two types of orbitals—an s orbital and three p orbitals, each of which can hold two electrons. Therefore a total of eight electrons can exist in the second shell. The third electron shell contains one s orbital, three p orbitals, and an additional five d orbitals and thus can hold a total of 18 electrons. The fourth, fifth, and sixth shells each have one s orbital, three p orbitals, and five d orbitals, together with seven f orbitals and thus can hold 32 electrons.

Understanding electron shells and subshells is important for understanding the periodic table. The table's pattern and arrangements not only follows atomic number, it also reflects the arrangement of electrons in the atom. As atomic number (and so the number of protons) increases, so too does the number of electrons. They fill the shells and subshells in a predictable way. The first row involves only two elements, since only two electrons can fit into the sole s orbital of the first shell. The second row has eight, representing the filling of the s and p orbitals of the second shell. One might expect the third row to have eighteen, but it turns out that d orbitals in the third shell have a bit higher energy than the s orbitals of the fourth shells and so are filled after them. Something similar happens with the f orbitals of the fourth shell, which begin to be filled in the fifth row. The presence of eight electrons in the s and p orbitals of the outermost shell is particularly stable and is achieved in the last column (the inert gases).

Meanwhile, elements in the same column (or group) have the same number of electrons in their outermost shells. This ranges from one in group 1 to eight in group 18. The elements in groups 3 through 12 and the lanthanides and actinides have incomplete inner shells and their chemistry is a bit more complex. Valency, the principle on which Mendeleyev relied, can be explained by understanding the outermost shells. Valency depends on the number of electrons required to be lost or gained during a reaction, thus leaving the outermost shell of an elements with its s and p orbitals filled—a so-called complete octet.

The periodic table also allows predictions of the course of chemical reactions, based on an understanding of the location and numbers of electrons. For example, imagine a reaction between a group 1 element, sodium (Na), and the group 17 chlorine (Cl). Sodium has one electron in its outer shell; chlorine has 7. A reaction to produce sodium chloride sees an electron switch from the sodium to the chlorine, giving a pair of complete octets.

Looking again at the periodic table, it becomes clear how much information it contains. While each box includes the element's chemical symbol and atomic number, by understanding the table, the position of each element can reveal even more.

See also: ATOM AND MOLECULE • CHEMISTRY • MENDELEYEV, DMITRY

Personal digital assistant (PDA)

The personal digital assistant, or PDA, is a tiny, fully functional computer about the same size as a pocket calculator. The PDA was invented in the 1990s as an electronic replacement for traditional paper diaries and business notebooks. PDAs have since evolved into multifunctional devices designed to complement a desktop or laptop computer.

▲ *Palmtop PDAs use touch-screen technology combined with a large number of computing features to function almost like a small laptop computer, often with comparable processing power and memory.*

The PDA is one of the fastest-selling consumer gadgets in history. The first commercially successful PDA was introduced in 1996. It was small and light, easy to use, and could store thousands of appointments, contacts, and notes. Now, PDAs have many features, including e-mail and Internet access and digital music players. They can receive and process complex information and communicate with other computers and PDAs.

PDAs come in "handheld" and "palmtop" models. Handheld PDAs are larger and heavier than palmtop PDAs, and handheld models have a miniature keyboard. Rather than a keyboard, palmtop PDAs have a stylus to touch the screen or even write on it directly. This is called touch-screen technology. Most palmtop PDAs can interpret notes handwritten on the screen with the stylus. Eventually, most PDAs will incorporate voice-recognition technology, in which a built-in microphone and software convert spoken words into digital data.

PDA parts

All PDAs share the same main features: a microprocessor, an operating system (OS) with software, a liquid crystal display (LCD), memory, and batteries. The microprocessor coordinates all of the functions of the PDA. PDAs are powered by smaller, cheaper, and slower microprocessors than

standard desktop or laptop computers. The OS consists of instructions, programmed into the PDA by the manufacturers, which tell the microprocessor what to do. The OS runs color displays, graphics, miniaturized software packages, such as Microsoft Word, and other functions, such as built-in digital music players and movie players.

All PDAs come with some kind of personal information management (PIM) software for storing contact information in an address book, including names, addresses, telephone numbers, and e-mail addresses. PIM software also allows the user to make task lists, write memos, record and remind people about appointments (using clock and alarm functions), and make calculations. Additional software can be added to the PDA, including business programs, city guides and translators for travel, and video games.

A PDA usually comes with at least 2 megabytes (MB) of memory. One megabyte of memory can store up to one hundred e-mail messages and four thousand addresses. A PDA does not have a hard drive like a desktop or laptop computer. The PDA stores basic programs (address book, calendar, memo pad, and the OS) in a read-only memory (ROM) chip, the memory programmed by the manufacturers. Data and software added later are stored in the device's random-access memory (RAM). These programs take up large amounts of memory, so more advanced PDAs may have up to 32 MB of RAM storage.

▶ **Modern handheld PDAs look very similar to cell phones. Indeed, many are now being merged with cell phones, digital cameras, and music players in a single multipurpose package.**

DID YOU KNOW?

Touch-screen technology works because the plastic top sheet of the LCD floats on a thin layer of oil that rests on another sheet of plastic. Thin bars of silver ink create a voltage between the two sheets when pressure is applied to the screen. This is recorded by driver software, which obtains the X and Y coordinates of the point at which the screen was touched. The driver scans the screen thousands of times each second and sends this data to software for processing.

Data synchronization

PDAs are much more prone to losing data than desktop or laptop computers. Backing up (making a safe copy of) data to a desktop or laptop computer is therefore extremely important. The communication between the PDA and a computer is called data synchronization. This is typically done by cable through a serial or universal serial bus (USB) port on the PDA. Some PDAs have a cradle in which they sit while hooked up to a standard computer. Data can be synchronized between the PDA and the computer using appropriate software installed on both machines. The PDA assigns each record, such as an appointment or contact details, a unique identification number and notes the date it was created. The synchronizing software compares the record on the PDA to the one stored on the computer and accepts the most recent record. This

ensures that data can be backed up regularly in case a PDA is broken, stolen, or simply runs out of power.

In addition to being able to communicate using cables, many PDAs have ports that use infrared radiation (IR) to beam information to a PC or another PDA. Some PDAs also offer wireless methods, such as Bluetooth technology, to transfer information to and from a PC or network through a wireless Internet Service Provider (ISP), similar to those available on cellular phones. Some PDAs offer telephone modem accessories to transfer files to and from a PC or computer network.

Looking to the future

PDAs will continue to evolve alongside existing computing and mobile communications hardware. However, the PDAs of the future may have integrated capabilities if the rapid convergence of information technology continues. PDAs now incorporate cellular phones, digital cameras, mobile gaming, and video capabilities, and the range of utilities is likely to grow.

See also: COMPUTER • MOBILE COMMUNICATION • TELECOMMUNICATIONS • VIDEOPHONE

Pest control

Pests are organisms that attack and often destroy buildings, clothes, food, and furniture. Some pests attack farm animals and pets; others attack human beings. Many also spread diseases. So great is the damage done by pests that about one-quarter of the world's food production is either eaten or spoiled by them.

▲ *A farmer sprays a pesticide on lettuce growing near Yuma, Arizona. The spray contains chemicals that kill insects and other pests living on the crops.*

Most pests are insects, but eelworms (a plant parasite), rodents (rats and mice), and even some birds are also a threat. Since pests cause so much damage and disease, scientists are constantly looking for ways to combat these creatures.

What to do about pests

Before deciding how best to attack and destroy a pest, the life cycle of the organism must first be carefully studied. It is important to know at which stage in its life a pest does most damage. For example, many insects are most harmful just after they have hatched from their eggs and become caterpillars (the larvae of butterflies and moths), grubs (beetles), or maggots (flies).

Some pests live all their lives in one field; others fly, crawl, or hop in from elsewhere. A pest may attack one or several different kinds of plants, and it may feed on different parts or burrow into the plant. All pests also have natural enemies, and it is very useful to know which creatures these are. With all this information, plans can be made to combat the pests long before there are so many of them that they damage food and human health.

Ways of controlling pests

There are three basic ways to control pests. One is called "indirect control," in which the farmer changes the planting time or the placing of crops so that when the pests are active there is nothing for them to eat. Then there is "direct control," in which pests are directly attacked with poisonous chemicals. Lastly, there is control by natural enemies—biological control—in which the organisms and diseases that prey on pests are used against them.

Indirect control

Crop rotation is a good way of protecting crops against pests that either live in the soil or rest there during the winter. Potato eelworms are one example. If potatoes are grown in the same ground year after year, the number of potato eelworms will increase due to the plentiful food supply and will soon become a danger to the crop.

Crop rotation does not protect them against insects such as the Colorado beetle, however, since the beetles can fly from field to field. Nor does it protect against pests that feed on a range of plants, such as wireworms (larvae of click beetles), leather-jackets (larvae of crane flies), millipedes, and slugs.

Destroying weeds near crops can also help control pests. For example, one variety of flea beetle lives on wild mustard but also attacks root crops such as cabbages, rutabagas, and turnips. The beetles makes holes in the leaves of the plants.

Changing the time of sowing a crop can sometimes save it from a pest. For example, the fruit fly lays its eggs on oat seedlings. To protect an oat crop from the fruit fly, a farmer sows the crop earlier in the year. Then the plants will be old enough to withstand attack by the time the eggs of the fruit fly have hatched.

New plant varieties that are resistant to attack by pests are being developed by scientists. Some alfalfas, cereals, clovers, and potatoes can now withstand eelworms, and some kinds of lettuce and raspberries resist greenfly.

Often creatures that have become pests in homes, hospitals, food stores, and other buildings can be controlled by keeping places clean. Cracks and holes let in insects, mice, and rats. Piles of trash are used by other pests to build shelters during cold winters and nests in the spring.

However, indirect control methods work best only against a few pests. By far the most widely used ways of controlling pests are direct methods.

Direct control

Chemicals have been used in the fight against pests for more than one hundred years. At first, they were taken from plants that could protect themselves against pests. For example, the powdered head of the pyrethrum chrysanthemum and the roots of the derris plant contain powerful insecticides (chemicals that kill insects). Another natural pesticide is nicotine, taken from the tobacco plant.

The first effective artificial insecticide was dichlorodiphenyltrichloroethane (DDT), which was developed in Switzerland in 1939. It was a huge success against many kinds of insects, including Colorado beetles, fleas, lice, and flies. Unlike natural insecticides, DDT could be manufactured in vast quantities. One of DDT's greatest successes was to help reduce the number of malaria-carrying mosquitoes in many parts of the world. Unfortunately, mosquitoes have now built up a resistance to DDT, and its use on crops has been criticized because the chemical stays in the soil for so long. DDT is now banned from general use in the United States because of the detrimental ways in which it affects the environment.

In addition to the chemicals that are sprayed directly onto pests, there are insecticides that can be absorbed by leaves and roots and then spread to every part of a plant. Any insects eating the plant or sucking its juices are therefore poisoned. Other insects that do no harm to the plant or that eat the pests are spared, whereas sprayed insecticides often kill both harmful and useful insects. However, plants filled with pesticide chemicals are also too dangerous for humans and animals to eat.

Natural enemies

In nature, most pests are the prey of other creatures, known as predators, that kill them for food for themselves or their young. For example, hawks and owls are the predators of rats and mice. Greenflies, or plant lice, are a widespread problem. However, they have enemies that keep their populations in check. Ladybugs and lacewing

◀ *A farmer prepares pesticides designed to protect Florida orange trees from attack by medflies.*

▲ Some pests are plants themselves. The corn on the right is being drowned out by foxtail weeds. On the left, the weeds have been treated with a herbicide that kills the weeds but not the corn crop.

insects and their young feed on greenfly; tiny wasps lay eggs inside the bodies of the greenflies, and there is also a fungus that attacks and kills the wasps. A serious pest in tobacco fields is the hawk moth caterpillar, called the tobacco hornworm, which also feeds on eggplants, potatoes, and tomatoes. It is hunted by the paper wasp, which kills and cuts up the caterpillars and takes the pieces back to its nest as food for its offspring.

Insects also destroy weeds which, without any check on them, spread over huge areas. The tansy ragwort, brought into North America from Europe, was a pest until the flea beetles that kept them in check in Europe were also introduced.

DID YOU KNOW?

The introduction of certain diseases has also been used to keep pest populations in check. For example, the rabbit disease myxomatosis, spread by rabbit fleas, has been used in places such as Australia, where the population of rabbits has reached pest proportions.

However, the predators are often themselves at risk from insecticides. Widespread use of insecticides in apple orchards against the codling moth, for example, also killed the insect that kept the European red mites in check. The red mites then in turn became harmful pests. To overcome this problem, a range of pest control methods are being used that target just selected insects.

Using pesticides

Pesticides, which include poisons that kill creatures other than insects, are prepared in a number of ways. Those in powder or liquid form are mainly used to spray crops. Some are prepared to be used as smoke or mist. These pesticides have a greater coverage than liquids or powders. Powerful chemicals are also mixed with other substances, usually some kind of food attractive to the pest and used as bait to destroy it. Poisoned bran pellets kill slugs and snails, and warfarin kills rats, mice, and gray squirrels.

Few pesticides are used without being mixed first. Most have to be added to oils or water, or both, or mixed with dry materials and formed into small grains or granules. Some can be shaped into solid strips to be hung in homes and greenhouses. The strips give off a vapor that kills houseflies, wasps, greenflies, and other insects.

Ways of spraying

Machines have to be used for spraying pesticides. Some machines are small enough to be carried, and the spray is directed by hand. Others have to be mounted on tractors. Often the crops in orchards and fields are too tall, cover too large an area, or grow too close together for a machine to pass through. In this case, the spraying is done by light airplanes or helicopters.

Spraying from the air

Light airplanes are very useful when pests such as the locust spread over large areas. Locusts are perhaps the most feared of all pests, especially in the developing world. They consume all the leaves and fruit of any plant in their path. They gather in swarms so huge that they can literally darken the sky. The best time to attack locusts is when they are still growing, before they develop wings. Flying swarms can still be sprayed from airplanes, but this is dangerous because the insects may choke the aircraft's engine.

Where large numbers of pests, such as eelworms, have built up in the soil, tractors drag special machines over the land that pump liquid insecticide into the ground.

Buildings and storerooms can be treated with clouds of insecticide to destroy beetles and moths and their young and also the spider mites that feed on stored flour and grain.

Harmful pesticides

Most pesticides are tested to see if they harm humans and animals, but they can still be dangerous if they enter the body. Protective clothing should be worn by people who spray insecticides and care should be taken to apply pesticides only to the area they are meant to cover. Some pesticides remain active in the soil or are washed down rivers into seas. DDT-like substances, such as 2, 4-dichlorophenoxyacetic acid (2, 4-D) and dioxin, have been found to accumulate in wildlife and the environment.

Safer pesticides

As a result of the dangers of pesticides that remain active for many years, such as dioxin, scientists have been trying to find something else to use in place of the natural insecticides such as pyrethrum. Very large amounts of insecticides are needed to protect precious crops. Natural insecticides cannot be grown or made in the same large amounts as artificial poisons. Also, they break down and become useless after a short time, so crops have to be sprayed regularly. Chemical insecticides that act like pyrethrum (called pyrethroids) are even more powerful than pyrethrum, especially against beetles and caterpillars. In addition, they last longer and are less harmful to people and wildlife.

▶ *Several locusts feed on vegetation. Locusts are among the most devastating of insect pests.*

DID YOU KNOW?

Why have the powerful pesticides not already wiped out all the harmful pests in the world? One reason is that individual pests are not identical but slightly different from each other. A few individual pests will not be affected by the poisons that rapidly kill off the rest of the pest population. With all the other pests gone, these resistant individuals have plenty of opportunity to increase in number. Eventually, all of the pests in the area will be the resistant types, and this would render the pesticide useless. Farmers must be careful not to use pesticides too much so that they do not make the resistant population even larger. Scientists are always searching for new pesticides to avoid the overuse of one particular chemical and to prevent pests from becoming resistant.

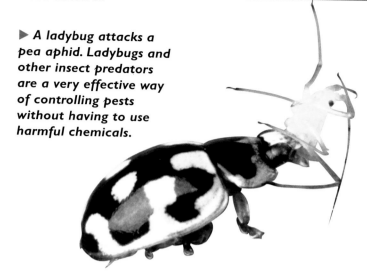

▶ *A ladybug attacks a pea aphid. Ladybugs and other insect predators are a very effective way of controlling pests without having to use harmful chemicals.*

Weed control

Weed control can mean anything from getting rid of everything growing on a piece of land to selecting just a few weeds to be destroyed. Weeds can be cut down, burned, dug up, or killed using chemicals. However it is done, it is an important and continuing job for farmers.

Almost any plant can be a weed, however attractive it may look. A weed is simply a plant growing in the wrong place. On a small patch of land, such as a garden, this problem can be solved easily just by pulling weeds up by hand or by turning over the surface of the earth with a hoe. This uproots the weeds and usually kills them.

There are many other machines used to control weeds, ranging from small handheld tools designed for gardeners to large machines drawn by tractors for use on farms. One of the oldest devices is the plow, which cuts into the ground, turning it over and slicing through the roots of the weeds. In cold weather, this is generally enough to kill most of them. Plows are also used to dig furrows—trenches in which the seeds of crops are planted.

Another method of weed control involves making a shallow cut in the soil and leaving a layer of weeds on the surface, which helps retain moisture in the soil. This is used in areas where soil erosion is a problem. Other methods of clearing land include flooding it for several weeks and burning stubble left after the crop has been harvested. This destroys young weeds before they have a chance to grow.

Chemical control

All the mechanical methods described so far are ways of clearing the land before the crop is planted. Once the crop has begun to grow, weed control becomes more difficult. The farmer has to find a way of removing weeds without damaging the crop. In this case, chemicals are used to control weeds.

A chemical used to kill weeds is called an herbicide. Herbicides were first developed in France in 1896, when it was discovered that copper sulfate ($CuSO_4$) would kill wild mustard without damaging the crops within which it was growing. Other chemicals, such as sulfuric acid (H_2SO_4), can be used in the same way. Although these chemicals are dangerous, they are still used in some places.

In the 1940s, a group of weedkillers known as auxin-type herbicides were developed. These are also called hormone weedkillers and are made from chemicals found naturally in plants. *Auxin* is another word for "plant hormone." The chemicals affect the way the plant grows. When the weedkiller is applied to the plant, it grows much faster than it is naturally able to, and this kills it.

The first auxin herbicides were particularly useful for killing broad-leaved plants, but other kinds, which selectively attack different kinds of plants, were soon developed. The herbicides are not usually poisonous to animals and do not stay active in the soil for very long, so they do not prevent other plants from growing.

The best known type of auxin weedkiller is 2, 4-D. However, there are many other herbicides that kill specific types of plants, as well as chemicals that will kill any type of plant. Common herbicides include sodium chlorate and paraquat.

The various selective herbicides work in many ways, not all of which are understood. Some work by disrupting the process of photosynthesis (the way plants use sunlight to manufacture food). Sometimes the herbicide is absorbed by the plant and carried to the roots, where it acts as a poison.

The way plants grow can make a difference to how herbicides work. Some affect only plants with broad, waxy leaves. Sometimes the position of the growing points of the plant—the parts of the plant where the leaves and stem begin—makes a difference. For example, grains have a growing point just under the ground, but the buds of broad-leaved plants are on the stem. So a spray that works only when it contacts the growing point will affect broad-leaved plants but not grains.

Dangers

Weedkillers must be used with care. They must be applied at the right time, and this is particularly important in the case of selective weedkillers, such as those designed to kill sprouting weeds before the crop is planted.

The conditions must be right, too. Some weedkillers need a certain amount of moisture in the soil before they will work, but too much rain simply washes them away. Other weedkillers will damage crops but not destroy them, so they should be applied only to the weeds as far as possible. Even auxin-type herbicides can kill any plant if the mixture is too strong, so it is important to prepare the mixture properly.

All herbicides are poisonous to some degree. But since mechanical methods of weed control can create problems, such as soil erosion, it is likely that farmers will turn to chemical methods of weed control. So it is important that experts know how to avoid the risks involved with using herbicides. For example, the poison paraquat is widely used and is deadly poisonous to humans, so it should be stored securely away from small children. When applied to weeds, it will kill them all, but it does not remain active for very long, so it is possible to grow crops on the land after it has been used. However, scientists are still researching the effect it has on the organisms in the soil, which play an important part in breaking down organic matter used by plants as nutrients.

Another herbicide, sodium chlorate, burns very easily, and the flames are difficult to extinguish. This can be especially dangerous when it is used, as it often is, to clear weeds from a building site.

It is important, too, to be aware of the effect that weedkillers can have on the ecology of the areas in which they are used. If all the weeds are removed, then the pests that once lived on the weeds may start eating the crops instead. Or, once weeds of one kind have been destroyed, another may become more common and take its place. This has sometimes happened when all the broad-leaved weeds have been removed from grain-producing areas. Weeds such as wild oats and other grasses, which are similar to the grain plants, have suddenly begun to thrive and have replaced the broad-leaved weeds as serious pests themselves.

Natural enemies

Other methods of weed control include introducing pests to eat selected weeds. In Australia at the beginning of the twentieth century, the introduction of the prickly pear created problems, because it had no natural enemies in its new home. The Argentine moth-borer, which attacks the prickly pear in its native South America, was introduced to Australia in 1926, and it almost entirely destroyed the prickly pears.

◄ *Mice are the most common pests in the home. They live wherever there are people, eating garbage and stored food. Rodents are controlled by laying traps or poisoned grain in the areas in which they are found.*

See also: AGRICULTURE

Pheromone

Many perfume advertisements are based on the idea that a special scent will attract the opposite sex. In fact, science has discovered that certain bodily chemicals, called pheromones, probably do make people react to smell in a sexual way. Pheromones are known to be important in the reproductive behavior of many animals.

The study of pheromones is a relatively new branch of behavioral biology, even though the existence of pheromones has been known for centuries. Pheromones are chemical substances produced by animals, which are released into the surroundings to attract sexual partners. This attraction system is used by animals that tend to live solitary lives and do not come across members of the opposite sex very often. Pheromones allow these animals to broadcast that they are ready to mate over a wide area. For example, male moths can detect the sex pheromones of female moths from 5 miles (8 kilometers) away.

Pheromones are used by invertebrates, fish, and mammals. For example, the musk deer of Asia is a mammal whose reproductive behavior relies on pheromones. Musk from the deer's abdominal glands has long been used to make perfumes. More sociable animals, including people, do not need pheromones to meet mates, since they live in large groups. However, scientists think that pheromones play a role in human relationships, too.

How pheromones work

Pheromones are released through pores in the surface of the animal's skin or in the sweat and urine. When another animal of the same species detects them, it reacts by changing its behavior, releasing pheromones in response or moving toward the sources of the smell.

▲ *The societies of honeybees, like those of ants, are controlled by pheromones produced by the queen. The chemicals are passed from one worker bee to another through bodily contact.*

In a similar way, pheromones play a major role in the way a queen bee controls her hive. She releases a pheromone from a gland in her mandible (mouthparts), and this secretion is passed along to the worker bees in the hive. The pheromone keeps other bees from laying their own eggs and makes them care for the queen's eggs.

Social insects, such as ants, bees, and wasps, are the most highly organized species in the animal kingdom. Every worker behaves in a way that fits the needs of the colony. Pheromones control their behavior. For example, the death pheromone tells ants to remove the body of a dead ant in their midst. The recognition pheromone enables them to recognize their own species. An ant will attack one of its own kind only if its antennas—the organs it uses to detect pheromones—are cut off.

▶ *This is a pheromone dispenser, which releases the sex pheromone of the female codling moth in orchards. This stops the moths from producing caterpillars that damage the fruit.*

Pheromones also play a part in the reproductive behavior of sea creatures, such as crabs and starfish, and land mammals such as otters and marmosets.

Pheromones and people

Glands in human skin release oils that keep the skin and hairs flexible and strong. In other mammals, these same glands play a part in the production of pheromones. There are two hormones that could possibly act as human pheromones. These are androstenal, which is related to male sex hormones, and androsterone. In experiments with pigs, breeders have successfully used androstenal to stimulate mating.

Androstenal has been found in human sweat and urine. Not everyone can smell these pheromones. Of those who can, not all say that the odors are pleasant. However, scientists now believe that the chemicals are detected by the nose, but the nervous system does not translate them into a smell. Studies have also shown that many people who have something wrong with their sense of smell lose interest in sex.

DID YOU KNOW?

Insects and many other invertebrates detect pheromones and other smells with tiny hairs on their antennas, legs, feet, and mouthparts.

Perhaps it is the amount of the pheromone that makes a difference. For example, most perfume has a "fecal (having to do with feces) note" in it. This is a rich, fatty smell. It would be revolting in large quantities, but perfume experts include a fecal note in most perfumes.

Aromatherapy is an unusual way of treating illness using the fragrant oils extracted from many different plants. Aromatherapists claim that their treatment will help with illnesses brought about by stress, such as asthma, and some forms of backache. They believe that pheromones act on people's emotions to help them recover.

Musk attracts

Musk was first used by the ancient Chinese for perfume about 4,000 years ago. In the 1960s, this scent became popular as a natural perfume. Its popularity spread and, by the 1970s, the production of musk had become big business. Most musk comes from the musk deer in the form of the hormone muscone. However, civetone from the civet cat also has a musklike smell, as does the glandular secretion from the American muskrat, which is a rodent that lives in rivers. Both of these scents are also used in perfume manufacture. Since natural pheromones are expensive to collect, there are many human-made versions used in perfumes.

See also: REPRODUCTIVE SYSTEM • SMELL

Phosphorus

Phosphorus is an element found in certain rocks in many parts of the world. It is also present in the bones of humans and other animals. It is used in fertilizers, because it is necessary for the growth of plants. Humans get most of the phosphorus they need from eating eggs, milk, meat, and fish.

In its pure form, phosphorus is a heavy, white, waxy solid that is extremely poisonous. It belongs to the same group of elements as arsenic and nitrogen. Phosphorus is normally stored under water or in oil because it burns slowly when it comes into contact with oxygen in the air. The solid melts at 112°F (44°C). When heated or exposed to light for a long time, white phosphorus changes into another form called red phosphorus. Red phosphorus behaves in a different way from white phosphorus. It is not poisonous and does not burn in the presence of air.

How phosphorus is made

White phosphorus is taken from phosphorite—a phosphate rock found in many parts of the world, including North Africa, Russia, and the United

▼ *Phosphorus compounds are used to make matches. Safety matches are lit by striking the match against a rough board on the side of the matchbox. This board is a mixture of sand and red phosphorus. Strike-anywhere matches have a phosphorus compound in their tips, which catches fire when drawn across a rough surface.*

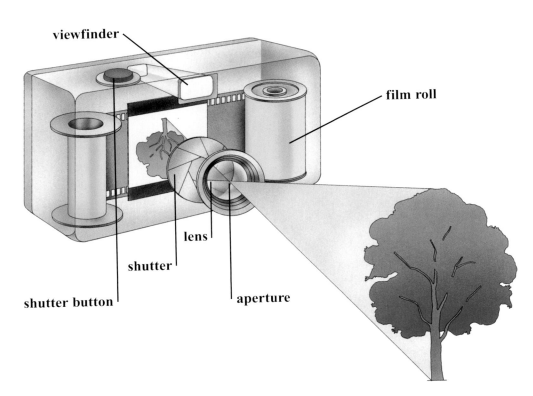

▶ *This diagram shows how a camera works. The camera lens focuses light from the tree and projects an upside-down image of it onto film at the back of the camera. The aperture (hole) behind the lens can be made larger or smaller to allow more or less light through. The shutter behind the aperture allows light to pass for the precise amount of time needed to expose the film.*

produced a blurred photograph. To overcome these problems, cameras were designed with adjustable shutters and lenses.

Shutters

Two main types of shutters are used in modern cameras. The interlens shutter is made as part of the lens unit. This type of shutter has moving metal blades that open and shut to let light into the camera. The exposure time can often be set between one second and a few hundredths of a second. Most cameras have fewer settings.

DID YOU KNOW?

The word *camera* comes from the Latin word for "room." The camera obscura, meaning "dark room," was the forerunner of photographic cameras. It has been used for more than two thousand years and works in the same way as a photographic camera, with light entering a dark room through a tiny hole. The light formed an image on the opposite wall.

Focal plane shutters are located just in front of the film. They consist of a pair of tiny roller blinds, which move across the film to make an exposure. A gap between the blinds exposes the film to light entering the camera. The amount of light that falls on the film can be varied by altering the width of the gap between the blinds. It can also be varied by changing the speed at which the blinds move. Most focal plane shutters give exposures ranging from one second to one thousandth of a second.

High shutter speeds are used when the subject of a photograph is moving quickly. A fast shutter can "freeze" the action. Slow shutter speeds are used to take pictures in dim light because more light gets onto the film. At speeds below one hundredth of a second, cameras need to be fixed to a tripod to prevent any wobbles from blurring the picture.

Diaphragm

Cameras have a device called a diaphragm fitted to the lens. The diaphragm provides an aperture (opening) through which the light passes. The size of the aperture controls the brightness of the image formed on the film when the shutter is opened. So, like the shutter, it is a way of varying the exposure.

◄ *This photograph was taken with a long exposure. The shutter was kept open for longer than usual so the light coming from moving objects, such as this amusement park ride, create a blurred image on the film.*

the lens can be used to focus light onto the film. This means that the photographer can choose which part of the image will be sharpest, even close-up objects. Often the lens is wound by hand into or out of the camera body to alter its distance from the film. In reflex cameras, the image seen in the viewfinder is the same as what is coming through the lens, so the photographer can see if the image is in focus.

Most modern compact cameras and many reflex cameras focus automatically. They do this by sending out an invisible beam, which reflects off the subject. The camera detects this reflection, measures how far in front of the camera the subject is, and positions the lens in the correct place.

Various combinations of opening and shutter settings are used to obtain the desired picture. A large aperture with a fast shutter speed can let in the same amount of light as a small aperture with a slow shutter speed. Having this choice gives the photographer great control over the pictures.

Depth of field

With a wide aperture, only objects within a limited range are sharp. This is called a narrow depth of field. It is useful for making one person or object stand out sharply against a blurred background. If, on the other hand, the photographer wants to show everything as sharply as possible, then a small opening would be used. The aperture is usually referred to in terms of an *f*-number (*f* stands for focal ratio). A large aperture has a small *f*-number, and vice versa.

Lenses and focusing

The simplest types of camera have a fixed lens. A small aperture ensures that most subjects produce a sharp image on the film. Only the closest objects are blurred. However, on more advanced cameras,

Focal length

The distance between the camera lens and the film inside a camera controls how large an image will be on the film. This is known as the focal length of the lens. A lens's focal length depends on its shape and size, and this affects how far it must be from the film to focus an image correctly.

The standard lens for a camera using 35-mm film usually has a focal length of 50 millimeters (about 2 inches) and so is called a 50-mm lens. It has an angle of view of about 45 degrees.

A camera lens takes in a certain area in front of it and no more, just as the eye does. This is called the angle of view, or the picture angle. The standard camera lenses give an angle of view about the same as that of the human eye. Therefore the picture taken through the lens shows everything in a natural perspective; everything appears in the correct proportion, as in real life.

Lenses of longer focal length than this have a narrower angle of view. They show a much larger (magnified) image in the viewfinder and therefore cannot capture as much of the scene as standard lenses. For example, a 200-mm lens on a 35-mm camera has an angle of view of only 12 degrees.

On the other hand, lenses with short focal lengths have wider angles of view. The image they produce is smaller than normal, but they can include more of the scene. Lenses with angles of view greater than 60 degrees are called wide-angle lenses.

There are two common types of lenses. A convergent lens concentrates light rays into one point. Convergent lenses are convex—they curve outward. When both sides are curved, they are called biconvex; if one side is curved and one flat, they are planoconvex. A divergent lens spreads light outward from the center. These lenses are concave—they curve inward. When both sides curve, they are biconcave. If one side curves inward and the other is flat, they are planoconcave.

Telephoto lens

To photograph an object some distance away, a lens with a long focal length must be used. Ordinarily, however, cameras would have to be much longer if the lens were to be the right distance from the film.

A solution to this problem was devised by British optician John Henry Dallmeyer (1830–1883). He built a compound lens camera, with a concave lens behind the normal convex camera lens. The concave lens made the light from the convex lens concentrate less quickly, thus giving a longer focal length; this was the first telephoto lens. *Telephoto* means "distant light." Telephoto lenses are used to take pictures of objects that are far away.

The distance between the two lenses in the early combination telephoto lens could be increased or shortened to get different magnifications. However, these lenses were very hard to use.

Modern telephoto lenses have the two lenses in a fixed position to each other. They are moved together for focusing, although the magnification

remains the same, which makes them easier to operate. (Dallmeyer's original telephoto lens combination, which could produce different magnifications, forms the basis of a zoom lens.)

Wide-angle lens

With a wide-angle lens on a camera, a photographer can take pictures of a wider area than normal—more than a person can see with the eyes alone. They are excellent for shooting in confined spaces, such as in a small room.

One of the most popular wide-angle lenses used is the 28-mm lens—with the relatively short focal length of about 1.1 inch. It has an angle of view of 74 degrees. The photographer can see much more of each scene, which shows up in the finished pictures. As the focal length gets shorter, the angle of view becomes even wider.

The limit of wide-angle lenses is reached at a focal length of about 0.6 inch—a 15-mm lens has an angle of view of 110 degrees. With this lens, the image is distorted, with straight lines looking curved.

Zoom lens

A zoom lens is a camera lens that can magnify objects by different amounts and can take the place of a number of separate lenses.

▶ *This is a single-lens reflex (SLR) camera with built-in flash attached at the top. This camera has a mirror inside that reflects the light coming through the lens into the viewfinder. This lets photographers see exactly what image will be formed on the film when they open the shutter. When the shutter is opened, the mirror is flipped out of the way. A range of lenses can also be screwed onto the front of the camera.*

▲ *Most modern cameras do not have films. They have light-sensitive electronics, which record the image as a computer file. Many cell phones are equipped with these digital cameras.*

The size of the image produced by an ordinary lens is fixed by the distance between the camera and the object. With any particular lens, the only way to change the size of the image is to move the camera closer to or farther away from the object.

For example, suppose a photographer is taking a picture of a bridge, using a camera with an ordinary lens, and the image of the bridge barely fits into the camera viewfinder. If the photographer then wishes to capture a small boat moored near the bridge from that same position, the boat will look very small in the viewfinder. To enlarge the picture of the boat to fill the viewfinder, the photographer must move much closer to the boat. However, to take a picture of a tree that the photographer is standing under, he or she must move much farther away from the tree to see the tree in the viewfinder.

The photographer could stay in the same place and change the lens on the camera, using a telephoto lens to photograph the boat and a wide-angle lens to photograph the tree. Alternatively, a zoom lens could be attached to the camera to photograph all three objects.

The focal length of a zoom lens can be varied, so it acts as many lenses in one. By lengthening the focal length, the photographer can "zoom in;" shortening the focal length is called "zooming out." Once the camera is focused correctly, it remains in focus as the photographer zooms in and out.

Using a zoom lens, it is possible to take a wide-angle shot of the crowd at a baseball game and then immediately switch to a close-up of the batter. It is not necessary to refocus each time.

How zoom lenses work

The zoom lens consists of many separate lenses called lens elements. They are mounted so that groups of these elements can move in relation to one another, and this changes the focal length.

A simple zoom lens consists of three lens groups—a divergent lens between two convergent lenses. The front convergent lens and the divergent lens may have to move different distances to keep the image in sharp focus.

In this design, the zoom mechanism includes a cam to move the lenses by different amounts, a method called mechanical compensation. In the most modern zoom lenses, however, the divergent lens remains fixed, while the others move together.

DID YOU KNOW?

The widest-angle lenses of all are called fisheyes. They are so called because of their highly curved front lens, which looks like the eye of a fish. The fisheye lens produces a round picture, and sizes and distances are highly distorted. The extreme 6-mm fisheye has an angle of view of 220 degrees. In other words, it can even see behind itself.

Flash guns

A flash gun is used to provide light for photography where the existing lighting is poor—such as indoors or outside at night. Flash guns may be used in strong sunlight, too. On sunny days, shadows are very dark. A brief, bright flash produced can light up these dark shadows to give a better picture.

Two main types of flash guns are used today. One takes flash bulbs, which give one flash only. The bulbs burn out rapidly with a bright flash. However, most modern flash guns have an electronic flash tube that can be used over and over again. Most cameras have built-in electronic flashes.

Many compact cameras used by ordinary people to take photographs, such as family portraits and holiday snapshots, are equipped with flickering flashes. These produce a short flicker of light before a single bright flash as the picture is taken, which prevents "red eye." Red eye is caused when light from the flash reflects off the back of a person's eyes. This makes the pupil, which is usually black, appear colored, usually red.

The flicker from the camera flash causes the iris to expand and reduce the size of the pupil—as it would in bright light. By the time the camera takes a photograph, the subjects' pupils are very small and do not appear colored, which would spoil the image.

Electronic flash

An electronic flash gun contains a battery and a flash tube. The flashes of smaller cameras are generally powered by the camera's main battery. The low-voltage current from the battery is converted into a much higher voltage, which is used to operate the flash tube.

The tube contains two metal plates in an atmosphere of rare gases. The plates, or electrodes, are connected to a large capacitor, which is a device that holds a charge of electricity. The capacitor is charged by the high-voltage current.

When the camera is operated, a pulse of electricity from a small capacitor is applied to an induction coil—a kind of transformer. This increases the pulse to several thousand volts, which is stored by a larger capacitor. When the flash is needed, the high voltage is applied to a metal electrode outside the flash tube, causing the gas inside to ionize, that is, the gas is converted into charged particles.

In this state, the gas is able to conduct (carry) electricity. When the high-voltage current from the capacitor connected to the electrodes inside the tube suddenly passes through the gas, the rapid discharge of electricity through the gas causes a bright flash. It takes a few seconds before the flash tube can be used again.

▶ *Press photographers, such as these at the tennis championships in Wimbledon, England, carry a variety of camera lenses to help them capture the best pictures. For photographing sports, powerful telescopic lenses are often required.*

Photographic processing

When a camera takes a photograph, the picture on the film cannot be seen immediately. The film must first be processed. This involves removing it from the camera and treating it with different liquids. These bring out the picture and make it permanent.

Photographic films must be processed in complete darkness because the film can still be affected by light. Once the pictures are taken, the film must never be exposed to light again, even for a fraction of a second, before processing is complete. The tiniest flash of light is enough to ruin the film completely.

Sometimes the film is kept in darkness in a special lightproof tank, or the whole room is blacked out to make a darkroom. Even when the film is processed in a tank, photographers usually work in a darkroom because the film must be moved from the camera to the tank in complete darkness.

In the early days of photography, films were not affected by light that was red in color, so photographers could safely use a red light—known as a safelight—when working in the darkroom. Modern film, however, is affected by light of all colors, so no light can be considered to be safe.

When film is processed, there are two main stages: developing, in which the image is brought out, and fixing, in which that image is made

▲ *Professional photographers use light meters to measure how much light they need to make a clear picture on the film.*

permanent (lasting). After each stage, the chemicals are washed off thoroughly. In the days when a red safelight could be used, photographers would simply look at the film to judge when to stop each stage and go on to the next. Today, however, the chemicals are kept at exact temperatures to make sure they always have the same effect. The photographer must time each stage very carefully.

Most amateur photographers take their exposed, undeveloped films to a studio or developers to be processed. This processing is often done at a central plant, where machines can process many hundreds of films automatically in a matter of hours.

A brief history

In 1727, German scientist Johann Heinrich Schulze (1684–1744) discovered that light darkened a solution of silver nitrate ($AgNO_3$). Then, in 1802, English chemists Humphry Davy (1778–1829) and Thomas Wedgwood (1771–1805) published their findings on how they had produced silhouettes of subjects by soaking paper and leather in silver nitrate and exposing them to light. Joseph-Nicéphore Niépce produced the first negative in

▲ *Many modern film cameras are very small. This compact camera has a viewfinder above the lens. The image seen though the viewfinder is slightly different from the one that is captured by the film.*

▶ *Modern camera film comes in two main formats—35 millimeter and Advanced Photo System (APS). The plastic film is coated with light-sensitive chemicals. APS films can capture images in three different sizes, but the quality is reduced compared to 35-mm film.*

1816 by placing a piece of sensitized paper into a camera. French painter Louis-Jacques-Mandé Daguerre (1789–1851) and English physicist William Henry Fox Talbot (1800–1877) took the next step in the 1830s by printing positives from the negatives. Daguerre used metal plates coated with silver iodide (AgI), and Talbot used paper soaked in silver chloride (AgCl).

U.S. inventor George Eastman (1854–1932) introduced roll film in 1888 and set up the Kodak company. He used an emulsion of gelatin and mostly silver bromide (AgBr) on a paper backing at first, but he soon used celluloid (a plastic) instead of paper. Color film for transparencies was developed in 1935; and, for negatives, in 1942.

Developing

Photographic film is covered on one side with millions of small silver bromide crystals, like tiny grains of salt. These crystals change color when exposed to light. When the camera's shutter opens, tiny specks of silver form on the surface of every crystal in the path of the light. These specks of metallic silver are so small that they cannot be seen, except under a powerful microscope. However, they are very important because they form an invisible record of the picture, called the latent image.

Growing crystals

When the developing chemicals are poured over the film, the specks of silver begin to grow. Some of the silver that makes the specks grow comes from the silver bromide crystals themselves. The developer contains chemicals that split the silver bromide crystals up, releasing solid silver. The rest of the silver comes from the developer itself. It is the silver that makes film and processing expensive.

Soon, the specks of silver have grown so big that they can be seen. Each single speck is still small, but together they form a picture. Where there are many specks, the picture is dark; where there are only a few, the picture is light.

Once development is complete, the picture could be seen on the film if the light was turned on. However, processing is not finished yet, so the film must still be kept in the dark because the silver

◀ *This machine is an enlarger. Light shines through a negative at the top of the machine. The light then falls onto light-sensitive paper underneath, making a positive image. The size of the positive image can be changed by adjusting the lens.*

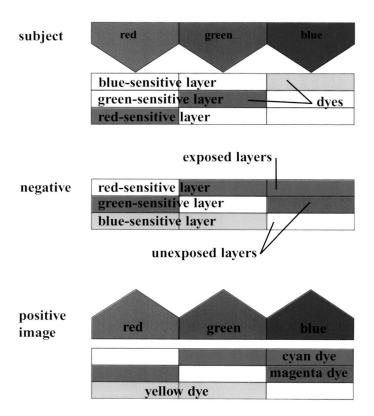

subject

| red | green | blue |

blue-sensitive layer	
green-sensitive layer	→ dyes
red-sensitive layer	

exposed layers

negative

red-sensitive layer	
green-sensitive layer	
blue-sensitive layer	

unexposed layers

positive image

| red | green | blue |

		cyan dye
		magenta dye
yellow dye	

▲ *This diagram shows how a slide film works. Dye is formed on the unexposed parts of the film. When combined, the layers reproduce the original colors.*

bromide crystals that are not part of the picture are still on the film. If they are exposed to light, the entire picture will become dark. So, before the photographer switches on the light, these crystals must be removed. This is the job of the fixer.

Fixing

Fixers work by turning the unused silver bromide crystals into substances that are not sensitive to light. These substances can then be washed off. The fixer has no effect on the silver specks.

The main chemical in the fixer is sodium thiosulfate ($Na_2S_2O_3$). Most fixers contain weak acid. The acid removes any developer still left on the developed film.

Color and similar films

Color films work in a slightly different way from black-and-white film, so they need different processing. They are called chromogenic (dye-forming), because the silver specks that make up the picture are replaced by dye patterns during processing. The image seen after processing does not consist of patterns of silver but patterns of dye.

All color film has three layers of silver bromide grains rather than just one. In color film, each of the three layers is sensitive to different colors—red, green, or blue. However, the layers are not colored themselves. In the developer, they form three images of silver specks, just like those on black-and-white film. The three images get their color during a second stage of developing.

Each crystal of silver bromide on the film is attached to a chemical device called a color coupler. When the exposed silver bromide crystals turn to silver, the waste products react with these color couplers, and dyes are formed. The dyes form only where the crystals turn to silver, so they form in exactly the same pattern as the silver specks. When the three pictures are seen together, the colors mix to show a picture of the scene in a variety of colors.

Similar to black-and-white film, however, the developed image is a negative. Thus, all the shades and colors are reversed. In the layer recording red light, a cyan (turquoise) dye is formed; in the layer recording green light, a magenta (purple) dye is formed; and in the layer recording blue light, a yellow dye is formed.

DID YOU KNOW?

The Schmidt camera is a telescope that takes photographs of vast areas of the sky. Large Schmidt cameras can show more than a million stars clearly. A Schmidt camera has a hemispherical mirror to focus light from the stars. The large mirror collects a lot of light from even the dimmest stars, but the light does not focus into a sharp image. In 1932, Bernhard Schmidt (1879–1935) invented a correcting lens to focus the light from the edge of the mirror to the same place as light from the center, making the image much clearer.

Processing is not over once the dyes are formed. The color film must be fixed to remove the unused silver bromide crystals. However, in addition to fixing, color film must also be bleached to dissolve the silver images, which are no longer needed. Usually, bleaching and fixing are done at the same time in a bleach-fix bath.

Negatives to positive

Printing is very similar to taking a picture with a camera. A machine called an enlarger is used. In the enlarger, light is shone through the fixed negative image onto a sheet of white paper covered in silver bromide crystals. A lens in the enlarger projects the picture onto the paper.

The print paper does not react to certain colors of light, so the photographer can use a safelight in the darkroom while printing. The image formed on the paper is a negative of the negative, so it shows the shades and colors in the right way—it is called a positive.

A slide, or transparency, uses film that produces a negative silver image. During development, the image is chemically reversed into a positive. For this reason, slides are called reversal film. The color couplers form dyes in the unexposed areas where no silver is formed. When the colored layers are combined, the image has the correct colors.

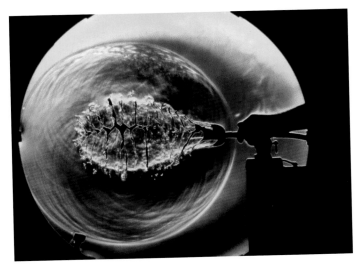

▲ This Schlieren photograph shows an air-filled toy balloon bursting from too much pressure.

Film negatives can also be scanned, with images printed directly onto photo paper using colored lasers or light-emitting diodes (LEDs). Computer software enhances pictures before printing to reveal more vibrant colors, richer detail, and fewer dark shadows than is possible with conventional film processing. This method can greatly improve prints of poorly exposed pictures.

High-speed photography

Some events—for example, a bullet leaving the barrel of a gun—take place more quickly than the shutter of a normal camera can open and close. Photographing events such as these requires high-speed cameras.

High-speed photography requires very short exposure times, so light will fall on the film for only a short time. To make up for this, the subject must be brightly illuminated by a flash. The flash needs to be triggered at exactly the same time as the picture is taken, providing a short burst of light. Strobe flashes, for example, are quite effective. They give four thousand flashes per second, one after the other, and can photograph rapid motion.

In a high-speed camera, the film passes through continuously, like in a movie camera. To prevent blurring, rotating mirrors and prisms—devices that bend light—are set to move at the same speed.

Schlieren photography

When people want to photograph colorless objects, they use Schlieren photography. For example, this technique can be used to photograph the air flowing around an airplane wing.

Schlieren photography comes from the German word for "streaks." This name comes from the flaws that the technique reveals in glass. A see-through material often bends light that passes through it. The amount of bending depends on the material. Schlieren photography detects the many different paths that light takes as it passes through a material.

See also: CAMCORDER • LIGHT • OPTICS • PHOTOGRAPHY, DIGITAL

Photography, digital

Digital cameras are rapidly replacing traditional film cameras. Rather than chemical film, digital photography uses electronics to record images. Digital images can be viewed on the camera as they are taken and can be easily manipulated using computers.

A major revolution took place in the field of photography in the mid-1990s. It became possible to take a picture using a digital camera rather than a conventional film camera. The big difference between a digital camera and a conventional camera is that there is no photographic film. Instead, images are captured electronically and turned into bits and bytes—a sequence of electrical information made up of 1s and 0s. Digitization was a turning point in the history of photography because a new photographic process was created. Digital photography dispensed with the chemical processes of developing film and turned the process of creating an image into an electrical one.

Every digital image consists of small dots, called pixels. The more pixels that an image contains, the better the resolution, which increases the quality of the final image. If a picture is taken using film, light comes through the lens and is focused onto a strip of light-sensitive film. The film is then developed through a chemical process, and an image is created. To see this image, it has to be either printed on photographic paper or scanned electronically. A digital camera cuts out the need for film or chemical processing. In a digital camera, light enters the lens and focuses onto a semiconductor, which turns light into an electrical charge. This information is processed by the camera's computer and turned into a picture.

The semiconductor

There are two types of semiconductors that turn light (photons) into electrical charges (electrons). Many cheaper digital cameras use a complementary metal oxide semiconductor (CMOS), but the most common type of semiconductor is called a charge-coupled device (CCD). CMOSs are less expensive to produce than CCDs but lack the quality required for higher-end cameras. Both of these semiconductor sensors work in similar ways, however, so to describe the process of digital photography, CCDs will be examined in this article.

▶ *This semiprofessional 5 megapixel digital camera has an optical zoom lens and conventional design. Because digital cameras work in a different way from traditional cameras, their designs can be more flexible.*

A CCD is a collection of tiny light-sensitive diodes that convert photons (light) into electrons (electrical charges). These diodes are called photosites. The brighter the incoming light, the stronger the electrical charge. Since photosites do not detect color, only the intensity of light, CCD sensors use filters that break down light into three different colors: red, green, and blue (RGB). Combining these colors can make any color of the spectrum.

There are several different ways of capturing RGB light on a digital camera. High-end digital cameras use three separate CCDs (a three-chip camera), each with a different color filter over it. Light coming through the lens is divided into three channels using a beam splitter. The advantage of having three chips is that it increases the amount of color information the camera receives. However, the three chips take up space and make the camera larger and more expensive.

Other methods of capturing color use just one CCD chip. One way is to cover the sensor with a variety of tiny red, green, and blue filters. Although each photosite is covered by a filter of only one color, it is surrounded by photosites with filters of other colors. This provides the onboard computer with enough color information to make an accurate guess at the true overall color of the image. This process of analyzing color information from groups of pixels is called interpolation.

Most cameras use the Bayer filter pattern, in which there is a row of red and green filters alternating with a row of blue and green filters. There are more green filters because the human eye registers more green than it does blue and red. Recreating a digital image as eyes would see it takes more green pixels than red and blue pixels combined. Once all the information has been gathered by a sensor, it is then turned into digital data for processing by the camera's computer.

Resolution

The resolution of a digital camera is largely determined by the amount of pixels that the camera's sensor uses to capture an image. This number usually varies between 1 million pixels

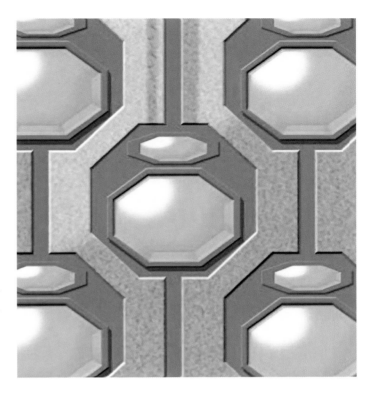

▲ **This illustration shows the pixels on a Fuji Super CCD SR. Unusually, the pixels are octagonal. This makes interpolation more accurate, as there are more points of comparison between pixels.**

(1 megapixel) to 14 million pixels (14 megapixels) or more. A megapixel is often abbreviated as MP. Sometimes two numbers are given in a camera's specifications—total pixels and effective pixels. The total pixels includes every pixel on the sensor surface, but usually the pixels at the very edges are not used in the final image. They are used for gathering other exposure information. The effective pixels are the number of pixels actually used in the image after the edge pixels have been discounted. This figure is more representative of the true resolution of a camera. Here are some typical resolutions of modern digital cameras:

640 × 480 pixels (307,000 pixels). This resolution is found in low-end cameras, such as those found in mobile phones. This resolution is suitable for e-mailing or use on the Internet.

1,216 × 912 pixels (1,109,000 pixels). This resolution (1 MP) is about the minimum required for making acceptable prints of pictures.

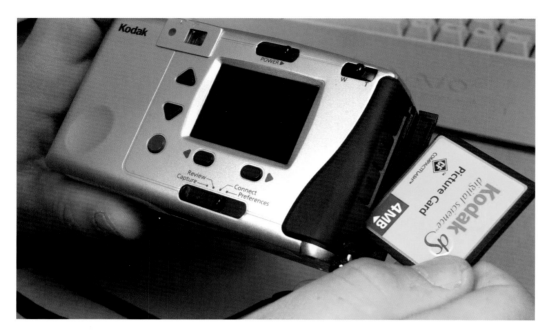

◀ *CompactFlash memory cards such as this are one of several formats in which digital cameras store image files. The number of images a storage device can hold depends on its capacity and on the file size of the images.*

2,048 × 1,536 pixels (3,146,000 pixels). This is a 3 MP resolution and is common on many compact digital cameras. A 3 MP camera can make excellent 4″ × 6″ prints and very good 5″ × 7″ prints.

2,592 × 1,944 pixels (5,039,000 pixels). Cameras with 5 MP resolution can be used for quality 8″ × 10″ prints. 5 MP sensors are found on high-end, fully featured digital cameras.

4,256 × 2,848 pixels (12,121,000 pixels). Sensors with very high resolutions such as this are found in professional digital cameras. These cameras are suitable for large prints and commercial projects.

The effective megapixel rating on a digital camera is a good indication of the quality of a camera. In general, the more megapixels, the better the camera. Professional cameras can reach a resolution of more than 15 megapixels. However, some traditional 35-mm camera film has a chemical grain approximately equal to 20 million pixels, so digital camera picture quality has to be improved before it equals the quality of film.

Picture storage

When a picture is taken, the information needs to be stored. Some of the earliest digital cameras had a built-in memory and had to be connected to a computer to download images. Most modern cameras have removable memory cards that use "Flash memory" to store the images. Flash memory cards act as small portable hard disks that, when full, allow the photographer to swap with another card or transfer pictures to a computer without moving or using the camera. Some of the different storage devices used in digital cameras include:

Built-in memory. Some basic, low-end cameras use only limited built-in Flash memory

SmartMedia. SmartMedia cards are small, thin, removable Flash-memory cards, available with average storage capacities.

CompactFlash. CompactFlash cards are another version of removable Flash memory. They are slightly larger than SmartMedia cards but are available with larger storage capacities.

Memory Stick. Memory Sticks are removable Flash-memory devices for Sony products.

Hard disk. Some professional cameras use small, built-in hard disks or hard-disk cards.

Writable CD and DVD. Some of the latest digital cameras use writable or rewritable CDs and DVDs to store image files.

Digital cameras use two main formats to store images. The first is the TIFF format, which is uncompressed; the second is the JPEG format,

Image Size (pixels)	TIFF (uncompressed)	JPEG (high quality)	JPEG (medium quality)
640 × 480	1.0 MB	300 KB	90 KB
800 × 600	1.5 MB	500 KB	130 KB
1,024 × 768	2.5 MB	800 KB	200 KB
1,600 × 1200	6.0 MB	1.7 MB	420 KB

which uses compression to make the image file size smaller. Most cameras use the JPEG file format for storing pictures; often they will offer quality settings such as medium or high.

The smaller the file size, the greater the number of pictures that can be stored on one device; but smaller size also means poorer quality.

Taking a picture

Like a traditional camera, when the take-picture button is pressed on a digital camera, two things happen. First, the aperture of the camera (the opening behind the lens) adjusts, letting light fall onto the CCD. The aperture works in the same way as the iris of an eye. On a cloudy day, an eye's iris expands, allowing more light in and enabling the eye to see more clearly. When it is sunny, the eye needs less light, so the iris contracts. The aperture of a camera performs the same job.

The second thing that happens is that the camera determines how long the CCD is exposed to light. On a sunny day, the exposure needs to be quick—perhaps a few hundredths of a second. In low-light conditions, the exposure needs to be slower to allow more light in (a few tenths of a second). In a digital camera, these procedures are done electronically rather than mechanically.

Most digital cameras automatically set aperture and shutter speed for the best exposure, which makes a point-and-shoot camera so easy to use.

▶ *Digital cameras such as this one can be made smaller than traditional cameras, allowing them to be extremely portable.*

▲ *This chart shows the relative file sizes of digital images stored at different levels of file compression. Uncompressed TIFF files take up more memory than compressed images, so fewer images will fit onto a memory card. Although uncompressed images are the best quality, images saved as high-quality JPEGs can be almost as good.*

DID YOU KNOW?

When buying a camera, it is best to choose one that runs on AA batteries, which are easy to replace. Buying rechargeable batteries will bring the cost down.

More sophisticated digital cameras offer the ability to adjust the aperture settings by using menu options on the camera's liquid-crystal display (LCD) panel. Professional photographers like to have control over the aperture and shutter speed, which gives them more creative freedom.

One of the great advantages of a digital camera is that the photographer can see the picture he or she has just taken on the camera's LCD panel. This

allows the choice of keeping the picture or discarding it and taking another one. However, there is a major drawback. LCD panels use up a lot of power and drain batteries very quickly. Some digital cameras have a built-in battery, but this can be frustrating as the camera must often be recharged. Other cameras have their own purpose-built battery, which tends to last longer, although buying spares is expensive. Some cameras are built to use standard AA batteries. These do not last as long as some specialized batteries, but they are much more convenient.

Lenses and focusing

The focal length is the distance between the lens and the image sensor (CCD). This distance is important because it determines the area that is photographed. With a traditional film camera, the focal length of a wide-angle lens (used for panoramic shots or large buildings) is around 30 millimeters. To take a picture of what the eye sees, a 50-mm lens is used, and for close-up shots a telephoto lens with a focal length of 105 millimeters or more might be used.

Since a digital camera's sensor is smaller than a frame of film in a film camera, the lens does not have to be so far away. On a digital camera, the focal length for a wide-angle lens is 5.4 millimeters, a normal lens is about 7.7 millimeters, and a telephoto lens is upwards of 16.2 millimeters.

A good lens is vital for picture quality. Inexpensive cameras have a fixed-focal-length lens. To change the framing of a picture, the photographer has to move backward and forward. An optical zoom lens allows the photographer to change the frame of the picture without moving the camera. By "zooming" in and out from a wide-angle to a telephoto view, the type and nature of the shot can be changed.

Some digital cameras offer a "digital zoom" facility. However, this only enlarges a picture that has already been taken, decreasing the resolution and creating a poorer quality image.

▶ *This picture is a screen shot of Adobe Photoshop Album. This popular photo-editing software can fix common photo problems, add a number of photographic effects, and create slide shows and greeting cards.*

◀ *This home photo printer combines dye-sublimation printing technology with built-in photo editing, so that no computer is required. Dye-sublimation printing creates pictures with 16.7 million colors at 403 dots per inch (dpi), rivaling traditional photo processing.*

The revolution in digital photography has sped up the process of taking a photograph so much that it has had huge implications in the professional world. For example, newspaper editors can get instant pictures of a breaking news story from almost anywhere around the world. The photographer can take a picture and send the digital image file by e-mail from his or her cell phone; the editor can have the image to use on the front page of the newspaper in a few minutes. Using a traditional camera, photographic film has to be developed, and the prints have to be made to send to the newspaper—a process that can takes hours if not days. The digital process has also had a huge effect on the costs of photography, eliminating the chemical photographic processing and enhancing desktop publishing and advertising.

With modern printers and paper technology, it is now possible to print photo-quality prints on even the most basic of printers. It is easy to print out duplicates and to reduce or enlarge prints at home. Printers with four or six individual ink cartridges produce the best quality prints.

As with most consumer electronics, the future brings smaller, cheaper cameras with better resolution. Electronics companies are looking to make the digital camera a "multimedia object:" a cell phone, an MP3 player, a personal organizer, and a video recorder, as well as a good-quality digital camera.

Image editing

Image-editing software, which manufacturers often provide with digital cameras, can give the photographer a wide range of creative choices. From simple things such as changing the brightness or contrast of a picture to more complex tasks like cropping images or adding filters (blurring or embossing), digital images can be given a new look. By manipulating the picture, its meaning can also be changed. Giving someone a different face or changing the look of his or her body creates an altered image. In the same way, imperfections in pictures, such as red eye, can be corrected easily.

DID YOU KNOW?

Some cameras offer an "MPEG movie" feature. This allows the camera to take a short movie. When buying a camera, look for the ability to change the resolution of the movie, and find out the longest movie length you can record.

See also: CAMCORDER • OPTICS • PHOTOELECTRIC CELL • PHOTOGRAPHY

Photosynthesis

Unlike people and animals, green plants have a food "factory" inside them in which they make their own food from sunlight, air, and water. This process is called photosynthesis. It is actually the basis of all life, because animals eat plants.

All living things need energy to power their growth and life processes. They get this energy by burning fuel, or food, a little like a non-living car engine does. Animals and most other types of living things get their food by eating other living things or their remains. Plants do not eat anything. Instead, they make their own food, using the energy in sunlight to power the process. The process is called photosynthesis (meaning "making with light"). Photosynthesis is the source of all food on Earth. Most animals eat plants. Without photosynthesizing plants, these animals would have nothing to eat. Animals that do not eat plants, such as lions or wolves, feed on the bodies of those animals that do. Without plants, these animals would soon run out of food, too.

▼ *Photosynthesis takes place inside leaves. The green substances in the leaves collect the energy from sunlight and use it to power food production.*

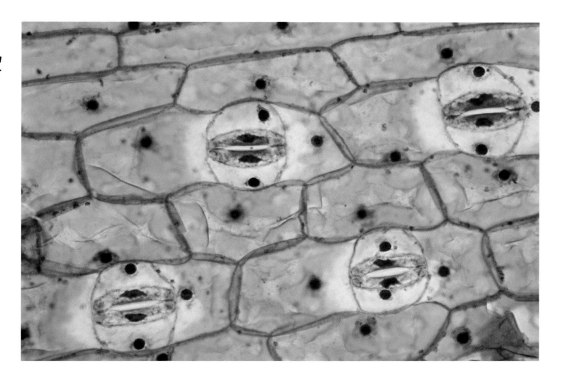

▶ *The darker cells in this microscopic image are guard cells around stomata pores on the underside of a leaf. The guard cells are sensitive to light and will contract to open the pores when the leaf is photosynthesizing.*

Sugar from air and water

Photosynthesis is a chemical process that combines carbon dioxide gas in the air and water from the soil into a sugar, called glucose. The reaction also produces oxygen gas, which the plant releases into the air. The energy needed for this complex reaction comes from sunlight.

Most photosynthesis takes place in a plant's leaves. The water needed for photosynthesis is collected by the plant's roots. This water is then carried to the leaves by a system of veins. The other raw material, carbon dioxide, is collected from the air by the leaves.

Light trap

The energy in sunlight is trapped by a green-colored chemical called chlorophyll. Sunlight is made up of many different colors, or wavelengths of light. Each wavelength contains a certain amount of energy. Blue light has the most energy, while red has the least. The color of an object depends on which wavelengths of light it absorbs or reflects. Chlorophyll makes leaves look green because it absorbs the red and blue light but reflects the green wavelengths. The energy in the absorbed light is used to power the many chemical reactions that take place during photosynthesis. Plants only make chlorophyll when they are exposed to light. Plants grown in the dark are therefore very pale.

Food factory

The structure of the average leaf makes it a very efficient food-making organ. Most leaves are flat and wide, which helps them trap as much sunlight as possible. The top of the leaf is covered in a waxy cuticle. This covering prevents the leaf from drying

---

DID YOU KNOW?

It is not just plants that photosynthesize. Bacteria and single-celled organisms called algae can do it, too. Algae have cells similar to those in plants, and they are equipped with chloroplasts. However, bacteria do not have chloroplasts. Instead, they make food with chromatophores. Biologists think that cyanobacteria (also called blue-green algae) were the first photosynthesizing organisms about 4.5 billion years ago. Their photosynthesis began adding the oxygen to the atmosphere that animals breathe today.

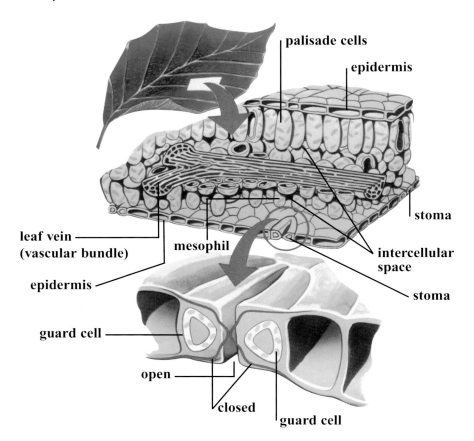

palisade cells

epidermis

stoma

leaf vein (vascular bundle)

mesophil

epidermis

intercellular space

stoma

guard cell

open

closed

guard cell

◀ *This illustration shows the parts of a leaf involved with photosynthesis. Leaves make the food that a plant needs by photosynthesis. The top red arrow points to the palisade cells in which this process takes place. The second red arrow indicates an enlarged stoma (plural, stomata), a tiny hole. Leaves have many stomata, which take in carbon dioxide from the air for conversion to sugars. They also release oxygen into the air, which comes up to the leaves from the roots and stem.*

out too much after being baked in the Sun all day. The cuticle may be hairy, which protects the leaf from drying winds, making it even better at holding its precious water.

The cuticle covers the epidermis cells. These are square or rectangular cells that form the thin upper surface of the leaf. Sunlight is able to pass straight through this layer. Beneath the epidermis are long pillarlike cells called palisade cells. These are filled with tiny structures called chloroplasts. Chloroplasts are made up of a stack of membranes, called the thylakoids. Chlorophyll molecules are attached to these membranes. The membranes are the site of the so-called "light reaction" of photosynthesis, in which the light energy absorbed by the chlorophyll is converted into chemical energy.

▶ *As well as being a raw material in photosynthesis, water is used by plants to fill the cells and give their bodies structural support. Water travels from the roots through hollow cells called xylem tubes located in the center of the stems and in a leaf's central rib. Xylem tubes inside tree trunks harden to become wood.*

Underneath the palisade cells are the spongy cells. There are large gaps between these cells, which provides room for gases to circulate around them. The gases get into the leaf through pores in the leaf's lower epidermis. A leaf pore is called a stoma (*plural*, stomata). The stomata are on the underside, because having open pores on the upper,

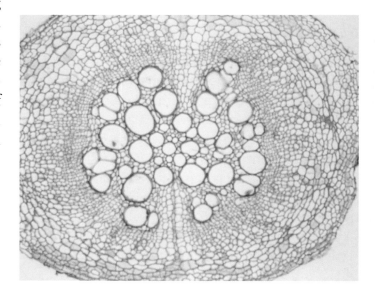

▲ *Many trees lose their leaves in the fall because it is too dark most winter days to photosynthesize efficiently. Dropping their leaves helps the tree save energy. Before the leaves fall, the tree absorbs the chlorophyll from them, to reuse next spring. The leaves then take on the yellow and brown colors of the chemicals that remain inside them.*

sunbathed side would dry the leaf out very quickly. Each stoma is made up of two guard cells. Like the palisade cells, guard cells have a lot of chloroplasts in them. When the plant is ready to photosynthesize, the guard cells contract. This contraction opens the stoma and lets the gases inside and outside the leaf to mix with each other. When the rate of photosynthesis slows as nighttime approaches, the guard cells expand and close the pore again.

Carbon dioxide in the air around the leaf diffuses (moves naturally) into the leaf, filling the spaces around the spongy cells. The palisade cells absorb carbon dioxide molecules and move them to the chloroplasts, where they react with water to make glucose and oxygen. This "dark reaction" is controlled by an enzyme (a protein that helps chemical reactions occur) called rubisco. (Biologists believe that rubisco is the most common protein on Earth.) The glucose is either burned for energy, or converted to starch for storage inside plant cells. The oxygen gas is released from the palisade cells, and it then diffuses out of the stomata into the air.

See also: CARBON • ENERGY • LIGHT • OXYGEN

Physical chemistry

Physical chemistry investigates the rules that control chemical reactions. Its aim is to discover how chemistry works. Recently, chemists have found new ways of studying what happens when one chemical mixes with another. Some of the reactions take place in millionths of a second.

Physical chemists study the way in which chemicals interact with each other. They look at what gives an atom its chemical properties, and how it reacts with another atom. Physical chemistry also involves how fast a reaction takes place, and how this rate is altered by changing conditions, such as the temperature or pressure. Physical chemists also investigate catalysts. Catalysts are substances that help other chemicals react with each other without being altered themselves.

People began to study chemistry scientifically in the early nineteenth century. One of the first to do so, and therefore one of the first physical chemists, was Amedeo Avogadro (1716–1856) of Italy. He suggested that a fixed volume of any gas, at a fixed temperature and pressure, would always contain the same number of particles. Avogadro's number, as this idea became known, paved the way for other chemists to figure out how the weight of an element was linked to its chemical properties. Russian chemist Dmitry Mendeleyev (1834–1907) used these ideas to draw up the periodic table of elements.

Modern physical chemistry

The basic tools of modern physical chemists are spectroscopy and X-ray diffraction. Spectroscopy analyzes the way chemicals give off or absorb light, which helps chemists understand how much energy is used to hold atoms together. X-ray diffraction involves passing a beam of X-rays through the chemical, to see how it is scattered by the atoms within it, allowing chemists to create a picture of how the atoms are arranged.

Physical chemists also use lasers to look at reactions as they happen. During reactions, some chemical bonds are broken and others are formed. It was once thought that a chemical bond broke so

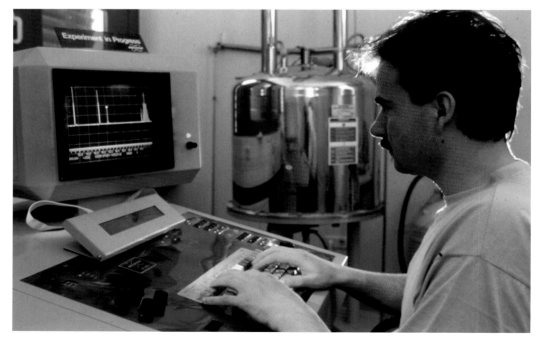

◄ *A chemist uses nuclear magnetic resonance (NMR) to study the atoms in a substance. NMR uses strong magnets and radio waves to determine the "chemical environment" of the sample. Each peak on the screen corresponds to a different environment.*

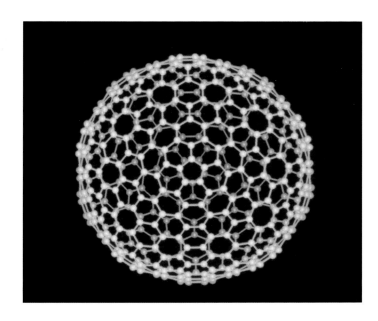

A computer graphic of a molecule of C_{540} fullerene. Fullerenes are being used to make ultrathin nanotubes. These hollow tubes of carbon might one day be used in computers or micromachines.

fast that it would be impossible to watch. However, lasers can be used to do just this. The technique is similar to the way a strobe light makes a person's movements appear to slow down. The strobe illuminates the person in short bursts, so an observer sees only the movements made during those illuminated periods. In the same way, the laser illuminates the reactions for just a short time, taking "snapshots" of atoms as they rearrange themselves during the reaction. Each burst of the laser lasts 60 femtoseconds. One femtosecond is a millionth of a billionth of a second. Reactions occur very quickly. They are all over in less than 10 millionths of a millionth of a second.

Physical chemists used lasers in another way in 1985 and discovered a new field of chemistry. They used a laser to vaporize pure carbon. They found ball-shaped molecules made up of exactly 60 carbon atoms. The carbon atoms were arranged into pentagons and hexagons, like the surface of a soccer ball. They named the molecule buckminsterfullerene for U.S. architect Buckminster Fuller (1895–1983). Fuller had invented geodesic domes, constructed like the carbon molecule.

Matching experiment with theory

The most common type of reaction is one in which atoms or molecules come together, react with each other, rearrange themselves, and then move apart in a different configuration. Although these reactions are taking place in laboratories all the time, chemists do not understand very well how they actually take place. It is easy enough to write down a chemical reaction, but showing how it takes place involves using quantum theory. (Quantum theory is a field of physics that describes how atoms are constructed out of smaller particles, and how these subatomic particles behave.) Computers can be used to calculate what is going on during a reaction, but accurate calculations generally take a very long time, even on the fastest computer.

So what chemists have done is to look at the simplest reaction, in which one hydrogen atom (H) is exchanged for another. The reaction is written down as $H + H_2 = H_2 + H$. The single hydrogen atoms consist of just one proton and one electron, so the number of particles involved is very low. This makes it much easier to apply quantum theory. By measuring how this reaction occurs, chemists can use the results to make their computer models of other, more complex reactions more accurate.

Chaos in chemistry

Some physical chemists are exploring the idea of chaos in reactions. Chaos theory looks at the way a small change at one point in a system can have a greater effect elsewhere. This occurs in systems with positive feedback, where the results of a change trigger more of that change to occur. This change could be a reaction that produces a material that acts as a catalyst, making the reaction speed up.

Chemists have looked at these sorts of reactions and have found that they can indeed show all the hallmarks of chaos. This has been surprising for many physical chemists, who thought that chemical reactions were always predictable.

See also: QUANTUM THEORY

Physics

Physics is the study of the materials and workings of the natural world and of the universe as a whole. Physics is a very ancient science. It is from physics that people have understood how electricity and magnetism works, what makes light come from the stars, why objects stay on the ground and do not float into the air, and many other facts that affect everyday life.

Physics is one of the two main physical sciences. The other is chemistry, which studies the composition of substances and the way they react with one another. Many areas of chemistry depend on physical laws. This has brought about the branch of chemistry called physical chemistry.

Physical chemistry investigates properties such as the rate of chemical reactions and how substances change chemically.

In the same way, the laws of physics are also used in other physical sciences, such as astronomy and geology, and even in life science, too. The special branches of these fields are called astrophysics, geophysics, and biophysics, respectively.

Astrophysicists study properties such as the composition, motion, temperature, and magnetism of stars and how they are formed. Geophysicists study, for example, the nature and formation of rocks in Earth's crust and the seismic waves produced by earthquakes. Biophysicists study things such as the circulation of blood and the

▼ *This archer is using laws of physics. By drawing the bowstring back, potential energy is stored in the bow. When released, the arrow is shot forward with kinetic energy. Aerodynamics helps the arrow fly straight.*

▶ *This picture shows* Integral, *the European Space Agency's International Gamma-Ray Astrophysics Laboratory. Highly sophisticated equipment such as* Integral *are at the forefront of modern physics.*

interchange of gases and dissolved substances in living tissues. Also, engineers apply many of the principles of physics when designing and building products and structures.

Classical physics

The science of physics had its beginnings in ancient Greece. Philosophers such as Aristotle (384–322 BCE) suggested theories to explain facts and events, called phenomena. However, these philosophers drew their conclusions as a result of logical arguments rather than by observation and experiment. For example, they would follow arguments such as: Earth must be a sphere because the sphere is a perfect shape and Earth must be perfect.

Such methods of explaining phenomena were clearly not scientific. Early studies of the natural world came under the heading of "natural philosophy." This term was used throughout the centuries until the 1600s and 1700s, when science started to separate from philosophy.

It was at this time, too, that the various fields of physics began to develop separately. Physics developed into what came to be called classical, or Newtonian, physics. It was named for English scientist Isaac Newton (1642–1727), who came up with many physical laws. He also devised (as did German mathematician and philosopher Gottfried Leibniz, 1646–1716) a new type of mathematics, called calculus, which could solve problems in physics that until then could not be solved. Classical physics includes the study of mechanics, optics, heat, sound, electricity, and magnetism.

Mechanics is the study of the behavior of bodies when they are acted upon by forces, and of the motion that these forces may give the body. The three fundamental laws of mechanics are Newton's laws of motion. Mechanics is subdivided into many branches. Kinematics is concerned with the

DID YOU KNOW?

Perhaps the best know physicist of all time is German American Albert Einstein (1879–1955). Einstein is most famous for his special and general theories of relativity. In these, he proposed that as objects travel at speeds approaching the speed of light, time, length, and mass can all change.

description of motion. Dynamics is the study of a body's motion with particular regard to the forces acting on it. Statics is a particular form of dynamics in which all the forces are in equilibrium and the body is at rest. There are numerous subdivisions of these branches, such as aerodynamics (the study of air in motion) and hydrostatics (the study of the forces acting in a fluid at rest).

The study of gravity also usually comes into this branch of physics. Again, Newton did all the pioneering study on gravitation, and he was able to explain in detail the orbits of the planets.

Newton also founded the science of optics (the study of light). He was the first to study the spectrum in detail and made the first reflecting telescope. His illustrious predecessor, Italian astronomer and physicist Galileo Galilei (1564–1642), also did much pioneering work in optics, as

> **DID YOU KNOW?**
>
> The most dramatic and deadly use of physics is in nuclear weapons. These are explosives in which devastating energy is released by nuclear fusion (the joining of nuclei) or fission (the splitting of nuclei).

he had done in mechanics. Galileo constructed one of the first practical refracting (lens) telescopes. One main branch of optics is geometric optics, which is concerned with the tracing of light rays and the formation of images by lenses and mirrors. The other, physical optics, is concerned with the behavior of light as a wave motion and studies phenomena such as interference and diffraction.

The science that studies sound is called acoustics. Acoustics developed in the eighteenth century when experiments were conducted to establish the speed of sound. It was not until the 1870s that the subject was discussed fully by English physicist Lord Rayleigh (John William Strutt; 1842–1919) in the book *The Theory of Sound*. One major branch of modern acoustics is ultrasonics, which is the production and use of sound waves of very high frequency and used in sonar devices.

The study of electricity began in ancient Greece. There, people were familiar with the electric charges that could be caused by rubbing a substance such as amber. The word *electricity* comes from the Greek word *elektron*, meaning "amber." It was not until about 1600, however, that there were experiments into electrically charged bodies, a branch of electricity called electrostatics.

In 1800, Italian scientist Alessandro Volta (1745–1827) made the first electric battery, and the first practical applications of electricity began to be developed. Within a few decades, physicists realized that electricity and magnetism are closely related and the term *electromagnetism* was born. In the

◄ *The uneven reflections from the glass of this office building can be explained using the physical laws of reflection and refraction. The scientific study of light is called optics.*

▲ *The MLX01 experimental maglev train on the Yamanashi Maglev Test Line, Japan, uses the physical properties of superconducting magnets to float above the track and propel forward at high speed.*

1860s, Scottish physicist James Clerk Maxwell (1831–1879) provided the mathematical basis for electromagnetism. This led to the idea of electromagnetic radiation—of which light, radio waves, and X-rays are examples.

Modern physics

The study of a different type of radiation by French physicist Antoine-Henri Becquerel (1852–1908) in the 1890s led to the study of radioactivity and the concept of a divisible atom. As conceived by English scientist John Dalton (1766–1844) in his celebrated atomic theory (1803) and some two thousand years earlier by Greek philosopher Democritus (c. 460–c. 370 BCE), the atom was the basic particle of matter. By 1911, New Zealand–born English physicist Ernest Rutherford (1871–1937) proposed his theory of atomic structure, which laid the foundations for modern theories of matter. A new branch of physics—atomic physics—was developing.

Classical Newtonian physics fails when it comes to explaining what goes on in an atom. Activity in an atom can be understood only in terms of the quantum theory, which was developed in 1900 by German physicist Max Planck (1858–1947) to explain the radiation of energy. At the atomic level, Newtonian mechanics has been displaced by quantum mechanics.

The nucleus of the atom has been found to be far more complex that Rutherford ever suspected. The protons and neutrons attract each other through the exchange of particles called mesons, of which pions are the simplest. The protons, neutrons, and pions themselves appear to consist of more fundamental particles called quarks. Evidence for these comes from experiments in which elementary particles collide at high energies. This branch of physics has become known as high-energy, or particle, physics as a result.

See also: ATOM AND MOLECULE • ELECTRICITY • ENERGY • MASS AND WEIGHT • PARTICLE PHYSICS • PLASMA PHYSICS • RELATIVITY

Physiology

In contrast to anatomy, which is about how living organisms are put together, physiology is the study of how living organisms work. Physiology is about how parts of organisms work together to perform particular tasks—from digestion and excretion to metabolism and photosynthesis.

Physiology is about all the chemical and physical processes that go on inside living organisms. Physiologists study the basic functions of living organisms—growth, metabolism, movement, and reproduction—and try to understand exactly how each biological process works at every level, from the entire body system right down to the individual molecules in cells. Physiology is especially concerned with how the human body works and is linked to anatomy and medicine.

Physiology has three main branches. General physiology is about the basic processes of life common to all living things, such as the way proteins are made. Functional anatomy is about how processes work in humans or particular animals. Plant physiology is about how plants work, including processes such as photosynthesis.

▼ *A great deal of the physiologist's work is done in the laboratory, using sophisticated equipment to analyze detailed chemical changes in cells and fluids taken from living organisms.*

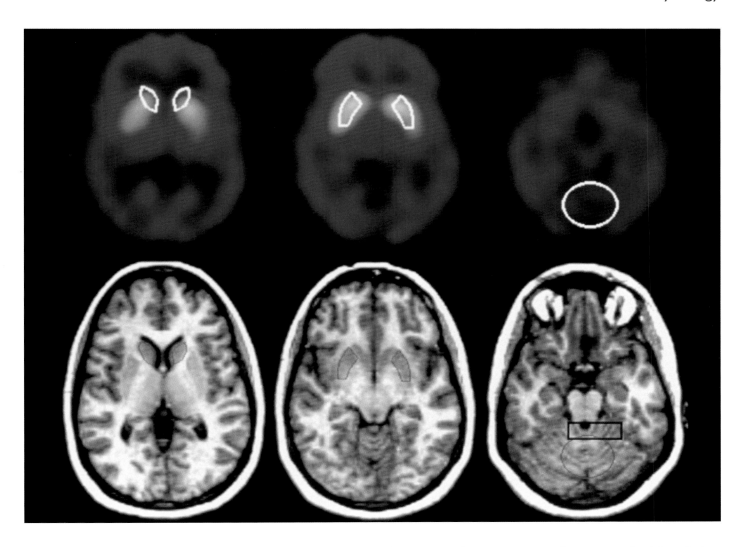

▲ *Brain scans enable physiologists to identify areas of the brain linked to particular functions—and actually see them become active in living patients.*

The study of physiology dates back to the first century CE, when Greek scientist Hero of Alexandria performed experiments on the bodies of living criminals. However, modern physiology began with the discovery of the blood circulation by English physician William Harvey (1578–1657) in 1616. Since then, physiologists have studied everything from the mechanisms governing metabolism and respiration to the role of chemical messengers, called hormones, in the body and how the nervous system transmits signals.

In recent years, huge advances in technology have enabled physiologists to study how the human body works in entirely new ways. New kinds of imaging devices have enabled them, for the first time, to study processes as they occur inside a living body. For example, incredibly powerful electron microscopes have enabled physiologists to see what is going on inside individual cells, right down to the molecular level. Indeed, many of the latest advances in physiology have come from studies of the cell.

Knowledge of physiology has been a tremendous help in the treatment of various diseases. For example, knowledge of the ways in which the blood circulation and nervous system work has helped physicians find the best way of treating brain damage, heart disease, hypertension (high blood pressure), and strokes. Studies of cell division have also helped physiologists understand why some cells become cancerous.

See also: BIOCHEMISTRY • CELL • DISEASE

Piezoelectricity

When a substance is put under pressure, it may change its shape. Under these conditions, certain substances that do not usually carry electricity may produce a small electrical current. This is called the piezoelectric effect, and it is used in various ways to reproduce sound.

Everything in the universe consists of tiny particles called atoms. Dipoles are atoms arranged in pairs—one with a tiny negative electrical charge and the other with a tiny positive electrical charge. If pressure is applied to material consisting of dipoles, the positive and negative atoms can be separated. During the separation, one side of the material becomes slightly more positive, while the other side becomes slightly more negative. This effect is called charge separation, and it creates a difference in voltage. The reverse also occurs. When a voltage is applied across a piezoelectric crystal, the crystal changes shape.

Whether a material is piezoelectric or not depends on the arrangement of its atoms. Sometimes the atoms in a crystal make a pattern that looks the same, no matter which side is viewed by the observer. This kind of pattern is called a symmetrical arrangement. Other crystals have an unbalanced pattern, with one type of atom positioned on the right when observed from one side but placed on the left when observed from another side. This kind of pattern is called an asymmetrical arrangement. If the atoms of a crystal have a perfectly symmetrical arrangement, then its charges cannot be separated by pressure.

Symmetrical and asymmetrical crystals

Common salt (sodium chloride; NaCl) is a perfectly symmetrical crystal in the shape of a cube. Sodium has positive atoms at the corners of the cube and in the center of each face. The positive sodium atoms are balanced by the negative chloride atoms in the middle of each side and the single chloride atom in the middle of the cube. Barium titanate ($BaTiO_3$) is an asymmetrical crystal with a rectangular shape, so it does not look the same from each side. The asymmetry of the crystal means that barium titanate is a piezoelectric material and will generate electricity when the crystal is placed under pressure.

Crystals exist in 32 different forms, each with its own arrangement of atoms. Twenty of these forms are asymmetrical, and so the crystals that take these forms are piezoelectric materials.

Piezoelectric materials

Quartz was the first known piezoelectric material. However, it did not produce very much electricity in relation to the amount of pressure applied. So other materials were developed with large crystals,

◀ *This is a close-up photograph of a quartz crystal used to keep time in a quartz watch. The crystal vibrates with complete regularity at a particular frequency as part of an alternating current circuit.*

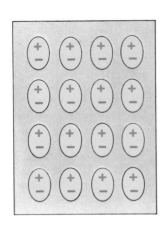

1. heteroelectret with no stress and no charge separation

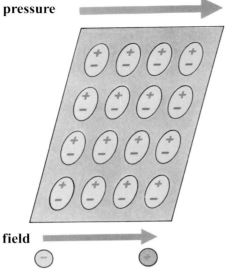

2. stressed material with charge separation

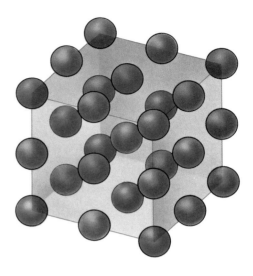

3. common salt

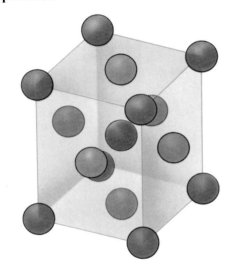

4. barium titanate

▲ *These diagrams show how piezoelectric crystals work. When a pattern of dipoles with their positive and negative poles all lined up (a heteroelectret, 1) is put under pressure (2), one end of the material becomes slightly negative and the other slightly positive. This cannot happen with common salt (3) because its crystal is symmetrical. However, barium titanate (4) is not symmetrical, so it is a piezoelectric crystal.*

such as ammonium dihydrogen phosphate (ADP; $(NH_4)_2HPO_4$) and sodium potassium tartrate ($KNaC_4H_4O_6.4H_2O$). These materials have some disadvantages, for example, they are not very strong. The largest class of piezoelectric materials in use are ceramic oxides, which have tiny crystals.

Uses of piezoelectricity

Piezoelectric materials are useful in situations where mechanical energy has to be changed into electrical energy, or vice versa. Devices that do this are called transducers.

A microphone is an example of a transducer. Movements in the air—the mechanical energy of a sound—must be turned into electrical energy so that the sound can be amplified (strengthened). Another transducer is the photocell in a compact disc player, which changes variations in the intensity of reflected light into an electrical signal.

Other piezoelectric transducers are used to transmit and receive sound waves through water. Since piezoelectric crystals work better at high frequencies, they are useful in ultrasonic equipment, such as cleaning devices. Sonar equipment that measures the depth of water or locates fish or submarines also uses piezoelectricity.

In the home, high-voltage piezoelectric devices are used to ignite cigarette lighters, electrical heaters, and natural gas stoves. Tiny transducers are used to measure the pressure changes in human blood vessels caused by heartbeats.

See also: CRYSTAL • ELECTRONICS • TRANSDUCER

Pipeline

Pipelines have been in use for thousands of years to carry water. More recently, the demand for oil and natural gas has led to the construction of pipelines thousands of miles long. Now engineers can even lay pipelines across mountains and oceans.

The easiest method of moving large quantities of material over a distance is by pipeline. Most pipes carry liquids, such as water or oil, or gases. However, pipes can also carry solid material in the form of slurry. Slurry is made of fine solid grains mixed with a liquid, making an oatmeal-like substance. Iron ore, coal, and limestone are all carried in pipes as slurries.

History of pipes

Pipes made from bamboo or clay were used 6,000 years ago in China. The ancient Romans used lead pipes to carry water. Many of their systems were vast. The pipelines that supplied the city of Rome, for example, were 380 miles (612 kilometers) long in total and carried 320 million gallons (1.2 billion liters) of water. Up to the nineteenth century, wood and lead pipes were used around the world.

Early pipelines were laid so that the water would be carried through them by the force of gravity. Modern pipes are made from cast iron, aluminum, plastic, and even concrete. Although the effect of gravity is still an important factor in pipeline design, modern pipelines have pumping stations to push liquids against the pull of gravity if needed.

Many of the longest pipes in the world carry oil and gas. These are built from steel and must be strong enough to withstand high pressures. Pipe sections are produced by rolling flat steel plates into

▶ *This oil pipeline in Alaska is raised above the ground to prevent the warm oil inside it from melting the frozen ground and causing erosion.*

tubes and then welding (uniting by heating) the edges together. These individual pipe sections are then welded together to form a very strong pipeline. Smaller pipes can be made by drawing steel out into seamless tubes. Another form of pipe is made from strips of steel wound into a spiral.

Oil and gas pipelines

Oil was first produced commercially in the United States during the 1860s at Titusville, Pennsylvania. The first oil pipeline was 5 miles (8 kilometers) long. It was used to carry 800 barrels of oil a day to the railroad. As the demand for oil and natural gas increased across the world, pipeline systems were built in areas where these products were plentiful, such as in North America and the Middle East.

▲ *A plastic pipe is lowered into a ditch by a crane near Athens, Greece. This pipe is flexible and light enough to be laid in long sections. Larger metal pipes are laid in shorter sections and joined together on site.*

Pipelines are now used to carry oil and gas from the wells to refineries or seaports, where huge tankers can dock to pick them up. Some pipelines are thousands of miles long. In North America, one stretches for 1,775 miles (2,856 kilometers) and runs from Edmonton, Alberta, in Canada to Buffalo, New York, in the United States. It carries nearly 7 million gallons (26.5 million liters) of crude (unrefined) oil each day. Another pipeline reaches from Siberia, carrying fuel all the way across Russia and into eastern Germany.

Pumping stations

The contents of pipes are pushed along pipelines by pressure from pumps. (Gases are often pushed through pipes using jet engines like those used to power aircraft.) A pipeline may have several pumping stations along its length. Each station is operated from a central control room. Many use computers to ensure that the flow through the pipe is even. This is particularly important where the pipeline is being used to carry more than one type of fluid. Batches of different fluids are separated by round inflatable balls called "batching pigs," which fit tightly into the pipeline. The "pigs" travel through the pipeline between each batch of fluid, preventing the batches from mixing together.

Laying pipelines

The methods of laying modern pipelines are very complicated and specialized. On land, they are generally buried underground, often under farmland. To allow farmers to plant crops or graze animals above a pipe, the pipelines are buried at least 3 feet (1 meter) underground.

Where seas have to be crossed, the pipes are laid on or under the seabed. Once the pipeline has been laid, it is often difficult and expensive to make repairs. So pipelines have to be built and laid according to certain requirements. For example, they have to be protected against corrosion, such as rusting. On land, pipes are painted or wrapped in

◄ *This large concrete-coated pipe is being laid between Hong Kong Airport, which is on an artificial island in the sea, and the mainland. The pipe will carry freshwater to the airport.*

felt and glass fiber to stop water and air from rusting the steel. Underwater pipelines have a coating of asphalt (tar) or plastic. An outer coat of reinforced concrete is added. This not only gives the pipe added protection, it also makes the pipe very heavy. The heavy pipe sinks to the bottom and cannot be moved by strong ocean currents.

People who lay steel pipelines with welded joints are specially trained for this job. Usually there are several teams used to lay a pipe. One team clears the route, another digs the ditch, and a third welds the pipe sections together and lays them in the ditch. The final team restores the land to its former state.

Before being put into use, a new pipeline is tested by pumping water through it under pressure to check for leaks and other weaknesses and flaws. Then any obstructions that might be left inside the pipe are cleared away by pushing circular disks through the pipe from each end.

Underwater pipelines

Constructing pipelines in water is a very different problem, especially when the pipes are wide and are being placed in deep water. There are several methods used to lay pipelines underwater. The lay-barge method was first used in the 1940s in the shallow waters off the coasts of Louisiana, Texas, and Venezuela. In this method, pipe sections are loaded onto a barge and welded together one by one. The pipeline is then trailed over the stern of the barge, which moves slowly forward, leaving the pipeline resting on the seabed behind it. Much smaller pipelines, up to 10 inches (25 centimeters) around, can be wound onto large reels and laid from the sterns of specially designed ships.

Another method involves welding pipe sections together on the shore and then winching the whole pipeline out into position. However, this method can be used only very close to the shore and where the seabed is flat and even. Otherwise, the surface tow method is used, in which the pre-welded pipeline is floated on the water using flotation drums. It is then towed out to sea and sunk into position. This method can be used only for fairly short pipelines. Floating longer pipelines would be too difficult to control.

In rough weather

The lay-barge technique has been greatly improved over decades. Since the discovery of oil in the North Sea off Scotland and Norway, special barges have been developed for laying pipes in deep seas and bad weather. To make it steadier in rough seas, a modern lay-barge is semisubmersible. It floats on huge hollow cylinders called pontoons that lie about 50 feet (15 meters) under the surface of the water. The barge is about 500 feet (150 meters) long and carries 7,000 tons (6,350 tonnes) of 40-foot (12.5-meter) steel pipe sections.

The pipeline is laid by a system similar to a factory production line. The sections are lifted, one by one, onto a conveyor and welded together. The welded pipeline is fed down a ramp toward the stern of the barge. Before the sections leave the barge, each joint is carefully X-rayed to check for cracks and then covered in asphalt or bitumen.

At the start, the pipeline is pulled out of the stern of the barge by an anchor attached to the first pipe section. However, as more pipeline is laid, its own weight pulls the new pipeline out. To prevent the unsupported pipe behind the barge from being damaged by the stresses caused by its own weight, the pipeline is fed out along a long, floating ramp called a stinger. This makes the pipeline form an "S"-shaped bend as it reaches down to the seabed.

The Trans-Mediterranean pipeline

Between 1979 and 1981, a 1,500-mile (2,500-kilometer) pipeline was laid from Hassi R'Mel in Algeria to Minerbio, near Bologna in northern Italy. Only 100 miles (160 kilometers) separate the coasts of Tunisia and Sicily, Italy, but in between lies a steep-sided trench about 2,000 feet (600 meters) deep. Previously, no pipeline had been laid below a depth of about 650 feet (200 meters).

The vessel that laid this pipeline was the *Castoro Sei,* one of the most advanced pipe-laying barges ever built. This vessel differs from other lay-barges in two important ways. First, instead of a stinger, it has an adjustable underwater ramp. The angle of the ramp can be varied anywhere from 9 degrees to 49 degrees. This allowed the *Castoro Sei* to lay the pipeline up and down the sides of the deep Sicilian trench. Second, the vessel has a highly advanced navigation system, which allowed it to stay in a fixed location. Normally, lay-barges use their

▶ *A section of pipe is added to a large underwater pipe inside a lay-barge. Once it has been fitted, the pipe will be fed out of the ship's stern into the ocean, and another section will be attached.*

anchor cables to hold them in position. However, the great depths of the Sicilian trench made it impossible for the *Castoro Sei* to rely entirely on anchor cables. The vessel's computer is linked to a mass of sensors that record every movement of the boat and control the amount of pull on the anchor cables, the amount of ballast (weight) in the pontoons, and the tension on the outgoing pipeline.

The pipeline operation was aided by a submersible (an underwater vehicle) that monitored how the pipe was resting on the seabed. The submersible also laid steel supports (with a secret design) in places where the pipeline had to cross steep-sided valleys. Remote-control explosive blasting systems were used to clear a way through rocky areas that blocked the path of the pipeline.

▼ *Sewerage pipes are stacked up at a construction site. When designing a new building, architects must plan where all the pipes are going to be located, since they are among the first things to be put in place.*

Pipe manufacture

Pipes are used in agriculture, mining, and other industries for carrying all kinds of fluids. They are used in homes to bring in water, and possibly gas, and remove sewage (waste water). Some modern pipes are manufactured from materials such as clay, metal, and concrete, but a large amount of piping is now made from different types of plastic.

Clay pipe

For the manufacture of clay pipe, clay is first ground to a powder and then mixed with water and chemicals to form a moldable mixture. This is then passed through a vacuum to remove air bubbles. The wet mixture is forced into a mold that has a solid central core surrounded by a hollow cylinder.

The pipe that comes out of the mold is then cut into lengths, trimmed, and dried. The pipes are then fired (hardened by baking) in a tunnel kiln, a kind of oven that may be over 650 feet (200 meters)

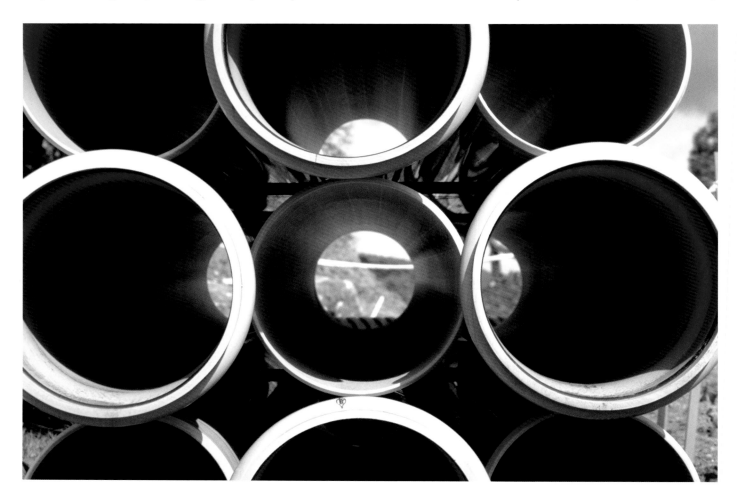

▶ *Plastic pipes are manufactured in a factory in Ghana. Plastic pipes are often used in place of metal ones, because they are light and flexible and do not corrode so easily.*

long. Cars on rails carry the pipes through a pre-heat section of the oven, then to the firing area, and last to the cooling section. The pre-heat stage uses hot air from the cooling area to heat the pipes to about 360°F (200°C). In the firing zone, the temperature is increased to 1980°F (1100°C) by oil or gas-fired burners.

Concrete pipe

Three types of concrete pipe are manufactured. Spun concrete pipe is made by spinning a circular mold filled with concrete. The concrete is thrown to the outside of the mold by centrifugal force, forming a compressed ring of concrete.

Prestressed concrete pipe contains steel wires that are pulled on as the concrete dries. When the concrete has hardened, the tension on the wires is released, which make the wires squeeze the concrete, making it even tougher than before. Prestressed concrete pipe withstand heavy pressure. Large water pipes are made of this type of material.

Plastic pipe

Most small pipes are made from plastic. Polyethylene, polypropylene, and polyvinyl chloride (PVC) are all thermoplastics. Thermoplastics are materials that become soft and moldable when heated up, which makes them ideal for making pipes.

In plastic pipe manufacture, the raw material is stored in the form of granules that contain the plastic mixed with colored chemicals and other substances called plasticizers. These make the plastic more flexible. The granules are taken to a machine called an extruder, where they are heated under pressure and become a large mass of plastic. This mass is then forced through a mold, and the soft pipe that emerges is cooled and hardened by water jets before being cut to the right length.

Plastic pipe is light and easy to handle. Polyethylene pipe is flexible and is used for narrow gas and water pipes. PVC pipes are generally less flexible but are tougher than polyethylene. They are used as large gas, water, and sewage pipes, household drain pipes, and electric conduits (surrounding electrical wiring in walls). PVC pipes are also being used to replace many of the old clay or brick drains used in farming and under roads.

See *also:* BUILDING TECHNIQUES • METALWORKING • OIL EXPLORATION AND REFINING • PLASTIC

Planck, Max

Max Planck was the brilliant German physicist who developed quantum theory. This theory revolutionized the understanding of the atom—and how things behave at the subatomic level— and overthrew people's common sense idea of how the universe works.

Max Planck was born in Kiel in Germany on April 23, 1858. He came from a very academic family. Both his grandfather and great grandfather were professors of theology at Göttingen, while his father, Julius Planck, was a distinguished professor of law at the University of Kiel. The young Max Planck was brought up in a home that placed great emphasis on scholarship, honesty, and generosity, and these values became deeply ingrained in his personality.

When Max was nine, the family moved to Munich, when his father was appointed professor there. The city provided a very stimulating environment for the young boy—its music, its nearby mountains, and, above all, the famous Maximilian Gymnasium, where he went to school. He was never a brilliant scholar. A school report for 1872 reads "justifiably favored by both teachers and classmates … and despite having childish ways, he has a very clear, logical mind. Shows great promise." But toward the end of his school career, he became interested in physics and mathematics.

Discovering heat

At the age of 17, Max went to university to study physics—first in Munich and later in Berlin. None of the teachers inspired him much. Then he read the essays of German physicist Rudolf Clausius (1822–1888), who wrote about how heat behaves. He wrote his thesis on the second law of thermodynamics—about how every time energy is used, some is lost as heat and cannot be used again.

▲ *Planck was a quiet man with a strong will and firm philosophical convictions. Despite his development of quantum theory, he refused to accept the more radical implications of the theory revealed by other scientists.*

Planck's ideas on thermodynamics quickly earned him a professorship first in Kiel, then in Berlin. It was in Berlin that Planck did his most brilliant research and gave riveting lectures on theoretical physics. A particular area of study was the distribution of energy at different wavelengths, and this was to lead to his development of the idea of the quantum. Planck was 42 when he developed his quantum theory and presented it to a meeting of the German Physical Society in December 1900.

Planck was, by nature, a cautious man, and he was very worried by the revolutionary nature of the theory he was proposing. He had believed entirely in the widely accepted wave theory of electromagnetism—the idea that electromagnetic radiation such as light travels in continuous waves.

But he could not ignore the evidence when he began to accurately measure the pattern of heat radiated from a black surface. It was clear that wave theory could not quite explain the pattern of heat radiation he observed.

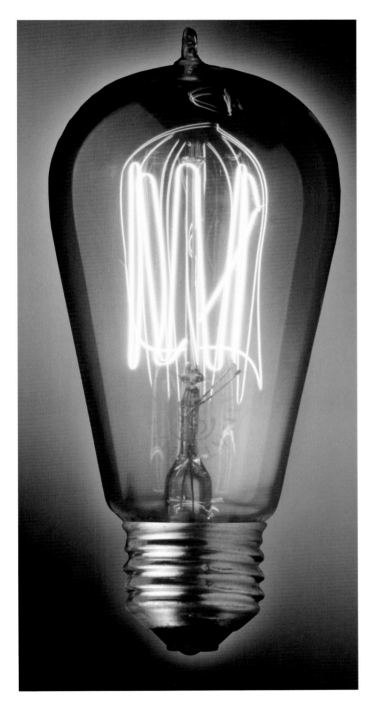

▲ *The filament of this electric light bulb is glowing with heat and light. Planck's study of the radiation of heat showed that radiation is not emitted in smooth, continuous waves, but in tiny chunks, or quanta.*

Chunks of energy

For a while, Planck worked hard to find the right mathematical formula to account for the pattern of heat radiated in terms of wave theory. But nothing seemed to work. Then he realized the observed radiation made perfect sense if it was emitted in chunks, or what he called *quanta,* from the Latin for "how much?" Quanta are very, very small. When many are emitted together, they seem like smooth waves; when they are emitted separately, they are like particles. It depends on how you look at it. Energy radiated as heat is always in perfect proportion to a particular number of quanta. So if you know how fast quanta are being emitted, you can calculate the energy exactly, and vice versa, using a set figure, which is called Planck's constant.

Planck's followers

Planck played only a minor part in the development of quantum theory and its astounding implications. Very soon scientists such as German-born U.S. physicist Albert Einstein (1879–1955) and Danish physicist Neils Bohr (1885–1962) began to realize that quantum theory applied to all particles smaller than an atom, and the science of quantum mechanics was born.

Quantum theory allows for all kinds of weird effects, such as particles appearing out of nowhere, or being in two places at once. Quantum theory has already led to the development of the laser. In the future, it may lead to even more amazing technology. Teleporting may seem like something from science fiction, but scientists have actually succeeded in teleporting particles. Using a phenomenon called quantum entanglement, particles are destroyed in one place, only to reappear instantly elsewhere.

Sadly, Planck's later life was filled with tragedy. His wife Marie died in 1909, one son died in World War I (1914–1918), both his daughters died in childbirth, and his son Erwin was executed for his part in a plot to assassinate Adolf Hitler. Planck himself died in 1947.

See also: HEAT • QUANTUM THEORY

Plant kingdom

The plant kingdom is a large group of living things that includes trees, flowers, ferns, and mosses. All plants survive and grow by harnessing the energy in sunlight in a process called photosynthesis.

All living things, or organisms as biologists call them, are divided into groups. These groups show how organisms are related to each other and how they have evolved. The members of each group share several common features, which they do not share with members of other groups.

The process of organizing groups of organisms is called classification. Classification groups have different sizes. The larger groups contain many smaller groups, which in turn are made up of even smaller sets of organisms. The largest classification groups are called kingdoms.

Most biologists agree that there are five main kingdoms. Two kingdoms include microorganisms made up of just one cell. These organisms are so tiny that they cannot be seen without a microscope. One of these kingdoms includes bacteria, while the other kingdom includes protists, such as amoebas and protozoans. (Some biologists suggest that these two kingdoms should be broken up into several others.)

The other three main kingdoms are made up of larger living things. They are the animal kingdom, the fungi kingdom (mushrooms and molds), and the plant kingdom.

What is a plant?

The scientific name for the plant kingdom is Plantae. As a general rule, all members of the plant kingdom share seven basic features. Although several nonplant organisms might also have one or more of these features, only members of the plant kingdom have them all.

▲ *Cacti, such as these in Utah, are examples of plants that have evolved to exist in harsh conditions. The bodies of cacti are able to store large amounts of water so that the plant can survive periods of drought.*

First, all plants are multicellular—they have bodies made up of many cells that work together to keep the plant alive. Second, all plants photosynthesize. Photosynthesis is a process that takes place inside many of a plant's cells. Photosynthesis uses the energy in sunlight to convert carbon dioxide (CO_2) and water (H_2O) into sugars. Plants capture the energy in the sunlight with colored chemicals called pigments. This energy is then used to power the chemical reactions needed to make sugar. Plants burn this sugar to release energy to power their life processes. The main plant pigment is called chlorophyll, which is green. A plant's leaves and stem are green because of the chlorophyll inside them.

Many types of bacteria and protists can also photosynthesize, although they often use different colored pigments to do it. However, since they are not multicellular, these organisms do not count as plants. In general, these photosynthesizing microorganisms are called algae. However, this term is not particularly accurate because they all come from many different classification groups, even different kingdoms.

Growth and movement

The third feature of plants is unlimited growth. Unlike the members of most other kingdoms, plants keep growing for their whole life, if given enough space. The fourth plant feature is that all their cells are surrounded by rigid walls. The walls are made up of cellulose, which is a substance that forms long chains. Millions of cellulose chains bind together to make a tough wall around each cell. It is these walls that give a plant its solid structure.

Another plant feature is that they are unable to move around, although some small plants may grow across a surface, with the older parts of the plant dying away. In this way, the plant may appear to be traveling very slowly. As well as lacking organs to move them about, all plants also lack senses and a nervous system.

Two generations

The final plant feature is called alternation of generations. This concerns the way plants reproduce. Every plant has two sets of genes—one from each parent. An organism with a double set of genes is described as diploid. Organisms with only a single set of genes are described as haploid. Most fungi and a few algae exist as haploid organisms.

> ### DID YOU KNOW?
>
> Not all plants can photosynthesize. Some plants do not contain green chlorophyll. However, all of these nongreen plants have evolved from green plants that can photosynthesize. Therefore, they are included in the plant kingdom.
>
> Nongreen plants get their food in one of two ways. Saprophytic plants absorb everything they need from the remains of dead organisms. These plants release chemicals called enzymes from their roots that break down the dead organisms. The nutrients released by these enzymes are then absorbed into the plant (the same way that fungi survive). Indian pipe is an example of a saprophytic plant that lives in North America.
>
> The other way nongreen plants survive is by being parasites. A parasite is an organism that gets its nutrients from another living thing, or host. Parasitic plants have roots called haustoria that grow inside the body of another plant, where they take water and food from the host. Parasitic plants include mistletoe (although this can also photosynthesize) and dodder. The world's largest flower—measuring up to 3 feet (1 meter) across—is produced by *Rafflesia arnoldii*, a parasitic plant from the rain forests of Sumatra.

During sexual reproduction, a parent transports one of its gene sets to combine with a set from another plant to make a new individual. Plants do this by forming two generations. The first generation is the sporophyte. Its cells are diploid. When it is time to reproduce sexually, the sporophyte produces another generation called the

◀ *These mosses are members of a class of plants called nonvascular plants. These are the simplest plants. Nonvascular plants typically live in damp areas where they can get the abundant moisture they require.*

gametophyte, which is haploid. Sex cells from two gametophytes then combine to make a diploid individual—another sporophyte.

In most cases, it is the sporophyte that is recognized as the plant. The gametophyte is very small and grows somewhere on the sporophyte. However, the two generations of many simpler plants grow independently of each other and can look quite different.

Plant diversity

Plants range in size from the tiny duckweeds, which are a fraction of a inch tall, to giant redwood trees, which grow to 360 feet (110 meters). Members of the plant kingdom fall into three main groups: the nonvascular plants, nonseed plants, and seed plants.

Nonvascular plants

Nonvascular plants, such as mosses and liverworts, are the simplest plants and were probably the first plants to evolve. They are described as nonvascular because they do not have vessels inside them that

DID YOU KNOW?

Early biologists often made mistakes when deciding if an organism was a plant or not. For example, until relatively recently, fungi were classed as plants. However, no fungi can photosynthesize. Instead, they are saprophytes, surviving on the decaying remains of dead organisms. Although a few plants also live in this way, it is now understood that fungi did not evolve from plants and therefore they make up their own kingdom.

Animals such as corals and sea anemones were first thought to be plants because they appeared to grow out of the ground and formed plantlike shapes. However, it was discovered later that they were in fact relatives of jellyfish. Many anemones and corals often have tiny algae living inside them, which photosynthesize and feed the host animal. This is an example of symbiosis.

Another example of symbiosis is seen in lichens. These often colorful mosslike organisms that grow on rocks are not plants, however. Instead, they are fungi and algae living together.

carry water and food around their bodies. Nonvascular plants do not have leaves, roots, or stems and do not produce seeds or flowers. Most are less than 1 inch (2.5 centimeters) tall because they lack the woody tissue necessary for support on land. They live in damp and shady places where they will not dry out.

Vascular plants

All other plants are vascular, meaning "with vessels." They have two types of tubes running from their roots, up their stems, and into their leaves.

◄ *This orange tree bears bright, juicy fruits. By producing edible fruits, fruiting plants can spread their seeds over wide areas. The seeds pass through animals' digestive systems and are deposited in their feces.*

▲ *This herb garden is full of plants that are useful to humans. Herbs are not only used in cookery, they are also used for medicine. Herbs have been used to treat illness for thousands of years, and many modern drugs are based on herbal compounds.*

Phloem tubes carry food in the form of sugary water around the plant, while xylem tubes carry water and minerals. Sugar is made in the leaves by photosynthesis and then passes into the phloem tubes. These tubes can be seen as the ribs and veins on the leaf.

The xylem tubes run alongside the phloem throughout the plant. The water and minerals travel from the roots, where they are absorbed from the soil, to the leaves through xylem tubes.

Seeds

Ferns and their relatives, such as bracken and horsetails, are nonseed plants. Instead of seeds, they release spores from cases under their leaves. The spores are haploid and grow into small gametophytes. Each gametophyte then produces a sporophyte, which grows into what is commonly recognized as a fern.

The seed-producing plants fall into two groups—the coniferous and flowering plants. Coniferous (cone-bearing) plants, such as pine and fir trees, produce seeds inside cones. The gametophyte generation is very small and grows inside the cones before producing seeds.

The seeds of coniferous plants (conifers) and their relatives, such as gingkoes and cycads, are naked—they do not have a covering. By contrast, the seeds of flowering plants are produced with a covering, often seen as a fruit or nut. Flowing plants make up the bulk of the plant kingdom. They make seeds inside their flowers, which contain the very small gametophytes.

See also: BIODIVERSITY • BIOLOGY • BOTANY • CELL • FUNGI KINGDOM • PHOTOSYNTHESIS

Glossary

Atmosphere The layers of gaseous chemicals surrounding Earth. The atmosphere provides oxygen and contains water vapor, which falls as precipitation. It also protects Earth from radiation and meteors.

Cam A machine component that either rotates or reciprocates (moves back and forth) to create a set motion in a contacting element known as a follower.

Crystal Any solid object in which an orderly three-dimensional arrangement of the atoms, ions, or molecules is repeated throughout the entire volume.

Diffraction The spreading of waves around obstacles. Diffraction takes place with sound, electromagnetic radiation (such as light, X-rays, and gamma rays), and very small moving particles that show wavelike properties (such as atoms, neutrons, and electrons).

Digital In communication, the representation of information as numbers. In computer technology, the representation of numbers as discrete units.

Emulsion A mixture of two or more liquids in which one liquid is present as droplets of microscopic size distributed throughout the other.

Excretion The process by which animals rid themselves of waste products and the by-products of metabolism. Processes of excretion in humans include exhalation, urination, sweating, and egestion (discharge) from the digestive system.

Fission, nuclear The splitting of large nuclei, such as uranium-235, accompanied by the release of vast amounts of energy.

Geometry The mathematics of the properties, measurement, and relationships of angles, lines, points, solids, and surfaces.

Gravity The natural force of attraction exerted by a massive body, such as Earth, upon objects at or near its surface, tending to draw the objects toward the center of the body.

Interference The combined effect of the intersection (crossing) or coinciding of two or more waves. The effect is that of the addition of the amplitudes (wave heights) of the individual waves.

Isotope Any of two or more forms of a chemical element with the same atomic number but different nuclear masses.

Metabolism Simultaneous and interrelated chemical reactions taking place in a cell at any one time.

Microprocessor A tiny silicon wafer containing millions of microscopic electronic components in an integrated circuit. Microprocessors, or microchips, are the "brains" of computers.

Momentum A property of moving matter that is defined as the product of its mass and velocity.

MP3 Short for MPEG-1, Layer 3. MP3 is a popular compressed digital music-file format.

MPEG Short for Moving Pictures Experts Group, MPEG was created by the International Standards Organization as a standard for compressing sound and movie files.

Photosynthesis The metabolic process by which energy from sunlight is converted into energy stored in chemical compounds. Photosynthesis occurs in plants and some types of bacteria.

Quanta Discrete natural units, or packets, of energy, charge, angular momentum, or other physical property. Light comprises quanta called photons.

Radiation Energy radiated or transmitted as rays, waves, or in the form of particles. X-rays and visible light are examples of radiation.

Respiration Metabolic process by which cells use oxygen, produce carbon dioxide, and store the energy of food molecules.

Static electricity Created when friction transfers electrically charged particles from one body to another.

Sterilize To rid of living organisms (especially microorganisms) by treating with heat or chemicals.

Vacuum A space entirely devoid of matter, or more generally, a space that has been exhausted to a high degree by an air pump or other artificial means.

Vapor The gaseous form of matter under certain conditions of heat and pressure so that it simultaneously exists as a liquid and/or a solid.

Index

Page numbers in **bold** refer to main articles; those in *italics* refer to illustrations.